D1374066

Methuen's Monographs on Biological Subjects

General Editor: G. R. DE BEER, M.A., D.Sc.

THE CHROMOSOMES

METHUEN'S MONOGRAPHS ON BIOLOGICAL SUBJECTS

F'cap 8vo., 3s. 6d. net each

General Editor : G. R. DE BEER, M.A., D.Sc.

Fellow of Merton College, Oxford

SOCIAL BEHAVIOUR IN INSECTS. By A. D. IMMS, M.A., D.Sc., F.R.S.

MICROBES AND ULTRAMICROBES. By A. D. GARDNER, M.A., D.M., F.R.C.S.

MENDELISM AND EVOLUTION. By E. B. FORD, M.A., B.Sc.

THE BIOCHEMISTRY OF MUSCLE. By D. M. NEEDHAM, M.A., Ph.D. (5s. net).

RESPIRATION IN PLANTS. By W. STILES, M.A., Sc.D., F.R.S., and W. LEACH, D.Sc., Ph.D.

SEX DETERMINATION. By F. A. E. CREW, M.D., D.Sc., Ph.D.

THE SENSES OF INSECTS. By H. ELTRINGHAM, M.A., D.Sc., F.R.S.

PLANT ECOLOGY. By W. LEACH, D.Sc., Ph.D.

CYTOLOGICAL TECHNIQUE. By J. R. BAKER, M.A., D.Phil.

MIMICRY AND ITS GENETIC ASPECTS. By G. D. HALE CARPENTER, M.B.E., D.M., and E. B. FORD, M.A., B.Sc.

THE ECOLOGY OF ANIMALS. By CHARLES ELTON, M.A.

CELLULAR RESPIRATION. By N. U. MELDRUM, M.A., Ph.D.

PLANT CHIMAERAS AND GRAFT HYBRIDS. By W. NEILSON JONES.

INSECT PHYSIOLOGY. By V. B. WIGGLESWORTH, M.A., M.D.

TISSUE CULTURE. By E. N. WILLMER, M.A. (4s. net.).

PLANT VIRUSES. By K. M. SMITH, M.A.

NEMATODES PARASITIC IN ANIMALS. By G. LAPAGE, M.A., M.D. (4s. 6d. net.).

THE CHROMOSOMES. By M. J. D. WHITE.

In Preparation

THE MEASUREMENT OF LINKAGE IN HEREDITY. By K. MATHER, B.Sc.

MYCORRHIZA. By J. RAMSBOTTOM, O.B.E.

Other volumes to follow

THE CHROMOSOMES

by

M. J. D. WHITE, M.Sc.

LECTURER IN ZOOLOGY, UNIVERSITY COLLEGE, LONDON

WITH 20 ILLUSTRATIONS

METHUEN & CO., LTD.
36 ESSEX STREET W.C.
LONDON

First published in 1937

PRINTED IN GREAT BRITAIN

INTRODUCTION

I HOPE that this book will be of use to many bio-
logists who realize that chromosome-cytology has
made considerable progress in the last ten years, and
that the existing text-book accounts of mitosis and
meiosis are hopelessly inaccurate, but who have no
time to read the larger works of Darlington and Bĕlař,
which must remain the standard sources of information
on the subject.

Chromosome cytology is essentially a practical subject, which can only be thoroughly mastered by a
study of actual preparations under the microscope.
Unfortunately this study is usually regarded as too
difficult to be included in a degree course in biology.
It is surprising, however, how much can be seen, even
without using an oil-immersion objective, provided
that one chooses suitable material with large chromosomes. There is no doubt that for most purposes the
testes of Locusts and Grasshoppers (any species will
do) provide the best introductory material. They
should be fixed in Flemming's solution and stained
in one of the aniline dyes like Gentian Violet. In the
course of the past year I have made the ordinary
degree students in this department work through
material of this kind (sectioned at $25\,\mu$ so as to
obtain whole nuclei). They were able to see all
the stages of mitosis and meiosis and even to work
out the average number of chiasmata per nucleus in
three different species. That it is possible for students
to do this in a course involving only one afternoon a
week should destroy the myth that cytology is a
fantastically difficult subject.

In a book of this size it is necessarily not possible

to quote ' chapter and verse ' for each statement. I mention this in apology for a certain amount of dogmatism imposed by limitations of space. The illustrations are essentially diagrammatic and designed to illustrate principles rather than to serve as actual illustrations of cell-division in particular organisms.

In any subject it is impossible to avoid technical terms, but I have endeavoured to reduce them to a minimum, and have explained in the text all those which are not self-explanatory. Where a term occurs for the first time and is defined it is printed in italics. In the description of meiosis I have adopted the term *bivalent* instead of *tetrad* as being far less likely to cause confusion. Barbarous terms such as ' heterotypic ', ' homotypic ', ' preheterokinesis ' and ' postacrosyndesis ' have done more to frighten the general biologist away from chromosome cytology than anything else, and those authors who introduced them must bear responsibility for the delayed integration of cytology into general biological knowledge. Only by a rigid avoidance of such terms can we hope to link up the study of the nucleus with colloid chemistry on the one hand and with animal and plant breeding on the other.

For those who find certain parts of the book difficult to understand, I would recommend the use of some models, which can be constructed in a few minutes out of soft copper wire or plasticine, using the illustrations as a guide. With the aid of these it should be possible for anyone to understand the details of chiasma-formation and meiosis.

Department of Zoology,
    University College, London,
April 1937.

CONTENTS

CHAPTER I

THE RESTING NUCLEUS

THE term ' resting nucleus ' is unfortunate, since it seems to imply that the metabolic activities of the nucleus are reduced to a minimum when it is not dividing—a view for which there is no evidence. The alternative term ' metabolic nucleus ' is equally unfortunate in that it suggests that dividing nuclei are physiologically inactive. On the whole it seems best to retain the established, although misleading, term.

The *resting nucleus* is, then, one which is not dividing. Usually it remains optically unaltered for long periods—it is not obviously changing either its shape or its appearance. This is, however, not always so ; many resting nuclei increase steadily in size (either by uptake of water or by actual ' growth ') and may alter their shape or appearance in various ways without dividing.

The chief structural parts of the resting nucleus are the *nuclear membrane*, the *nuclear sap* and the *chromosomes* ; these three constituents are always present—in addition bodies known as *nucleoli* may also be present. It has been suggested [31] that the latter are to be regarded as portions of cytoplasmic material included in the nucleus, but this is not so ; true portions of the cytoplasm may become accidentally included in the nucleus, and are then seen to be quite different in appearance from either nucleoli or nuclear sap.[175]

The nuclear membrane has been shown by microdissection to be a definite structure with physical properties. If a fine needle is gently pushed against

it, it becomes indented at the point where the pressure
is applied ; if the pressure is released it regains its
former shape ; if the pressure is increased it can
eventually be punctured.[23] The shape of the nucleus
undoubtedly depends in part on the properties of
the nuclear membrane. Most nuclei are approximately spherical, but many are ovoid. Those of
many Vertebrate leucocytes are in the form of a long
strand with periodic enlargements (Fig. 1a) while
those of the secretory cells of many insects are very
irregularly branched (Fig. 1b).[173] In all these cases
of non-spherical nuclei the nuclear surface is very
large relative to its volume, and it has been assumed
that this is connected with the process of secretion ;
but many secretory cells (such as the salivary gland
cells of Diptera) have approximately spherical nuclei.
Some unusual nuclei do not consist of a single body
at all, but of a number of separate vesicles, each containing a single chromosome and a certain amount of
nuclear sap inside a separate membrane (Fig. 1c).
In one case the sex chromosome is enclosed in a
separate membrane from the main nucleus (Fig. 1d).

The nuclear sap is usually a clear fluid ; its vis-
cosity has been determined in one case to be about
twice that of the water,[57] and this is probably
typical of most nuclei ; in some, however, the nuclear
sap may be a solid gel. The amount of nuclear sap
relative to the volume of the chromosomes varies
enormously from one type of nucleus to another.
Thus in the micronucleus of Ciliates and in the sperm-
head nuclei of many animals there is practically no
nuclear sap ; on the other hand, the total volume
of the young oocyte nuclei of birds (diameter up to
100 μ) may be 200,000 times that of the chromosomes
at metaphase.

The chromosomes may be, and usually are, invisible in living nuclei during the resting stage.[24,
60, 100] In some plant nuclei, however, and also in a
few animal nuclei, fine threads can be seen in the

living resting nucleus, which are almost undoubtedly chromosomes, although highly hydrated and almost

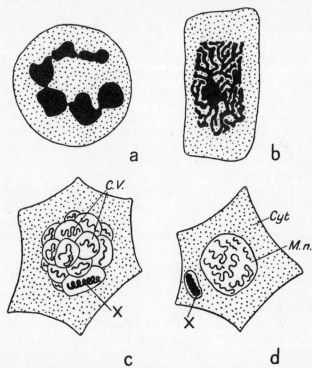

Fig. 1.—Unusual types of nuclei ; *a* in a vertebrate marrow-cell ; *b* in one of the spinning gland cells of *Platyphylax* (Caddis-fly) ; *c* in a spermatogonium of the grasshopper *Aularches* ; *d* in a spermatogonium of the Bush-Cricket *Pholidoptera griseoaptera*. In *c* each chromosome lies in a separate nuclear membrane, in *d* only the sex-chromosome lies in a separate membrane. Cyt. = cytoplasm ; C.v. = chromosomes lying in nuclear vesicles ; X = X-chromosome.

invisible, due to their having nearly the same refractive index as the nuclear sap. That the chromosomes do actually persist through the resting stage is

certain, since in some cases they become visible at the
beginning of one mitosis in the same position as they
occupied at the end of the preceding division.[13]
Also, in some cases special portions of chromosomes
persist in a condensed state throughout the resting
stage (*prochromosomes*).[44]

It is now becoming increasingly clear that no idea
of the structure of the resting nucleus can be obtained
from studying fixed preparations. The usual text-
book figure of a ' network of linen threads with
granules of chromatin at the points of intersection '
is meaningless save as a description of a gross artefact
which bears only the most remote relation to the
living structure. We must resign ourselves to the
fact that the resting nucleus and its chromosomes,
due probably to their high water content, are *unfixable*. It should be emphasized that this only applies
to resting nuclei—there is every reason to believe
that fixed preparations of nuclei in mitosis present a
very accurate picture of what is taking place in the
living cell (see next chapter).

Most cells in the body of an adult human being
have undergone about 50 mitoses since the fertilized
egg (i.e. an adult man consists of about 10^{14} cells,
making allowance for the erythrocytes, sperms and
other cells which are constantly being destroyed and
replaced). In the case of insects the adult cells have
undergone only about 20–30 divisions, and in the
case of the Nematoda and Rotifera still fewer. Between each of these divisions a resting stage has
intervened. These resting stages are, however, of
very uneven duration ; on the one hand two divisions
may follow on one another without being separated
by any resting stage at all (the end of one division
passing directly into the beginning of the next)—or on
the other hand the resting stage may last for years as
in many adult tissues of vertebrates. Many adult
cells may be said to have entered a permanent resting
stage, since they will never divide again. In most

cells the resting stage lasts a much longer time than the few hours required to undergo mitosis, but this is not always so. Some nuclei begin to undergo division and then become arrested, remaining in a particular stage of mitosis for the greater part of their life-cycle. Others may be caused to do so by specific chemical agents such as auramine, sodium cacodylate and colchicine.[102] The phenomenon normally occurs in some Ciliates of the family Opalinidae, where in different species the nuclei become arrested in meta-phase or anaphase and only subsequently resume mitosis after a long static period.[119] Moreover, in Vertebrate oocytes with much yolk (Sharks, Amphibia and Birds) the chromosomes may remain in one stage of meiosis for many months.[25, 154]

This naturally leads to a consideration of the question : what is it which causes a nucleus to leave the resting stage and enter on the complicated system of changes which we call mitosis ? In certain tissues such as cleaving embryos and frequently in lobules of the testis, division takes place synchronously in all the cells—that is to say every nucleus will be in exactly the same stage at any given moment. On the other hand in epithelia such as the skin and the gut-lining isolated cells enter on mitosis quite sporadic-ally and independently of the neighbouring cells. In the first case we appear to have a ' tissue-control ' of mitosis and in the second a ' cellular control '. Prob-ably in synchronously dividing tissues the substance which is inducing mitosis can diffuse freely from cell to cell (perhaps as the result of protoplasmic ' bridges ' between the cells), while in the second case it is unable to do so.

It must not be assumed that there is a single mitosis-producing agent. Possibly there is, but if so it is as yet undiscovered. But it is certain that a large number of physiological conditions are capable of stimulating cell division and it seems probable that in natural tissues more than one agency may be effective. In Fishes and Amphibia prolonged starvation followed by a meal may cause a considerable increase in the number of dividing nuclei, while in other cases starvation alone may be sufficient.[129] Such diverse stimulants as a peritoneal injection of foreign blood serum [48] or even a bacillus culture [75] have been found to produce the same effect. What the underlying chemical mechanism is in these cases we have no idea. It must be pointed out that a mere increase in the number of dividing nuclei in a histological section is not sufficient to prove that mitosis has been stimulated in resting nuclei ; it may equally well result from a slowing down of mitosis.

Gross mechanical injury to the nucleus such as results from the withdrawal of a microdissection needle previously inserted into the nucleus, will often produce a sudden acceleration of mitosis,[23] but in some cases it will cause the normal course of mitosis to be reversed, so that nuclei which have already entered on the division cycle go back into the resting stage.[174]

The effects of irradiation with X-rays also vary from one type of tissue to another. In some cases mitosis ceases altogether in a tissue for some days after irradiation ; cells which would have entered on mitosis are retarded in the resting stage.[117] In other cases X-rays probably accelerate the onset of mitosis. The whole subject of nuclear pathology is urgently in need of re-interpretation. Thus many nuclei when injured or dying become ' *pycnotic* ', that is to say their chromosomes become fused into a single large mass which stains intensely with dyes like Haematoxylin and anilin derivatives. Pycnosis is probably to be interpreted as a highly modified non-functional mitosis, since in some cases [147] pycnotic nuclei may begin to divide, but we do not know what actually happens to the chromosomes in a pycnotic nucleus.

Some recent authors have omitted the primary dis-

tinction between two forms of nuclear division,
mitosis and *amitosis*, regarding all kinds of amitosis
as merely modified or concealed mitosis. While it
is clear that most of the nuclear phenomena in
Protozoa which were formerly regarded as amitosis
are best considered in this light, there is no doubt
that true amitosis occurs in many somatic tissues of
insects (fat body, genital ducts, &c.). Here the
chromosomes probably divide and separate into their
halves in a ' resting ' nucleus and are then passively
distributed in approximately, but not exactly, equal
numbers to the two daughter nuclei into which the
original nucleus divides by elongation into a ' dumb-
bell ' shape.[114]

CHAPTER II

THE GENERAL OUTLINE OF MITOSIS

WE have seen in the previous chapter that the stimuli which can cause the onset of mitosis are extremely diverse ; they may be regarded as external agencies releasing an inherent chain of bio-chemical and biophysical events in the nucleus. If the cell is almost ready to divide in any case, stimulation by a mitogenetic agent or puncturing the nuclear membrane will produce a more or less normal mitosis ; if the mitotic mechanism is not 'wound up' then pycnosis results. A study of the gross disturbances which lead to mitosis does not help us much to understand the internal causes normally responsible for the initiation of the whole cycle of events ; neither does it explain how in some cases that cycle may be interrupted at certain stages and then subsequently resumed.

It is usual to divide mitosis into four stages, *prophase*, *metaphase*, *anaphase* and *telophase*. For convenience in description it seems best to subdivide anaphase into two parts and to insert a stage which can be called *prometaphase* between prophase and metaphase.

1. PROPHASE

At the beginning of prophase the chromosomes become 'fixable'—that is to say their appearance in fixed material approximates closely to that seen in living cells by the most reliable methods of observation. This 'fixability' increases throughout prophase until at prometaphase and metaphase there is

every reason to believe that fixed and stained preparations give us an almost perfect picture of the appearance in the living state. In the majority of nuclei
(all those which have not got prochromosomes) the
fixability is zero during the resting stage—thus the
first sign of prophase is the appearance of visible
threads (chromosomes) in the nucleus in place of the
network which results from the fixation of a resting
nucleus.

The ' fixability ' of early prophase nuclei varies a
good deal, but appears to be correlated with the
volume of the nuclear sap in which the chromosomes
lie ; thus in the first spermatogonial division of the
grasshopper *Metrioptera* the nucleus is large and the
prophase chromosomes very ' fixable ' ; in the suc-
ceeding divisions the nucleus gets progressively
smaller and the chromosomes less fixable until the
sixth division when there is a sudden increase in the
size of the nucleus which is accompanied by an
increase in fixability ; the seventh and eighth
divisions again show small nuclei in which the early
prophase chromosomes fix badly.[183]

The question now arises : what is the physical
basis of this property of fixability·? There is considerable evidence that it depends on the degree of
colloidal hydration of the chromosomes. BÉLAŘ [23]
showed by experiments on the dehydrating power of
hypertonic solutions on the nucleus that the metaphase chromosomes contain less water than any other
nuclear constituent and we have reason to believe
that the resting-stage chromosomes are highly
hydrated, so one must infer that dehydration is one
of the processes involved in prophase.

In all cases the chromosomes at the very earliest
prophase are separate ; there is thus no ' continuous
spireme ' as described by some of the earlier cytolo-
gists (the oögonial nuclei of the scale insect *Icerya
purchasi* form a possible exception,[68] but the case
needs re-investigation). Further, the individual

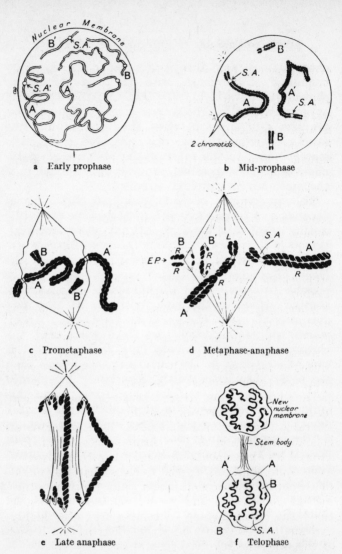

FIG. 2.—Diagrams of the main stages of mitosis. Only two pairs of chromosomes A and A', B and B' are shown. Both of these have sub-terminal spindle attachments, those of the B chromosomes being nearer the end. At early prophase the 'relic spirals' are clearly seen. S.A. = spindle attachments, E.P. = equatorial plane of the spindle. R and L are regions of the chromosomes which are spiralized in a right- or left-handed direction at metaphase.

chromosomes are always double from the very beginning of prophase, with the two threads or *chromatids* of which they are composed closely approximated throughout their length. Where there are size differences between the chromosomes the ratio of the lengths at early prophase is approximately equal to the ratio of the volumes at metaphase and it is possible to pick out the pairs of chromosomes in a diploid organism.

The appearance of early prophase chromosomes depends to a certain extent on whether the preceding resting stage has been of long or short duration. Where it has been short and the chromosomes are few in number as in the cleavage divisions of the Horse Roundworm, *Ascaris megalocephala*, it is possible to show [13] that the individual chromosomes become visible in the same positions as they had disappeared in at the previous telophase. Again, where the resting stage has been short and the chromosomes are relatively long and ' fixable ' it can be seen that at the early prophase stages they are coiled into loose spirals (Fig. 2a). Frequently each chromosome is not merely a ' spring ', but this spring itself describes a wide open spiral in the nuclear cavity ; in this case the smaller spiral has perhaps 5–20 turns, the larger one $1\frac{1}{2}$–2 turns. It appears that these two spirals are always in the same direction in a single chromosome, left- or right-handed, as the case may be.[34] The two chromatids are always closely approximated from one end of the spiral to the other.

As prophase proceeds the volume of the chromosomes increases considerably ; there is thus an actual manufacture of new material during prophase. Side by side with this a shortening and thickening of the chromatids takes place. We have thus identified three processes which are involved in the development of prophase : dehydration, growth, and condensation or contraction ; we must now add a

fourth—' despiralization '. That is to say that as
shortening and thickening take place the spirals of
the early stages unwind.[34] 725

In well-fixed chromosomes it is possible to see
from the very beginning of prophase that the staining
substance of the chromatids is not continuous from
end to end ; it is interrupted at one point at least
(in plant chromosomes usually several points) to
form a non-staining gap (Fig. 2). These gaps become
more obvious later, and are called *constrictions* :
their position is constant for each chromosome.
They are filled by a non-staining substance which is
not nuclear sap and which holds the chromatids on
either side of it together.

Throughout the prophase of mitosis the outlines
of the chromatids present a slightly irregular woolly
or hairy appearance which is probably an artefact :
they do not in general show a series of granules
(*chromomeres*) such as are seen at the meiotic prophase ; this may be a real difference and not due to
difference in fixability. By the end of prophase the
woolly appearance referred to above has almost
disappeared and a smooth outline has taken its
place.

The long threads of the early prophase chromosomes appear to wind more or less at random throughout the nuclear cavity ; but they never actually
come in contact with one another, or indeed approach
within a certain minimum distance : there is thus
something which keeps them apart, which is probably
in the nature of a generalized electrostatic repulsion
distributed over the surface of the chromosome. As
prophase advances there is a tendency for the
shortened and thickened chromosomes to move to the
periphery of the nucleus and to arrange themselves
on the inner surface of the nuclear membrane.

If a nucleolus or nucleoli are present in the resting
stage they usually lose their staining power during
prophase and have disappeared completely by pro-

metaphase. This is not the case, however, in many of the Protozoa, where what appear to be nucleoli often persist through the entire mitotic cycle.[4] In many cases nucleoli have been shown to be attached to particular pairs of chromosomes (e.g. the sixth in order of size in Maize) during prophase [40, 105]; apparently the point of attachment is always one of the constrictions referred to above. It has been stated that in these cases nucleolar material contributes to the growth of the chromosomes during prophase, but the evidence for this is unconvincing.

2. PROMETAPHASE

At the end of prophase the nuclear membrane usually disappears. In many of the Protozoa, and even in some higher forms, however, it persists and the whole process of mitosis is intranuclear.[4] The term prometaphase designates the period from the dissolution of the nuclear membrane up to the end of the process of spindle-formation. In ' intranuclear mitosis ' there is no stage which can be separately distinguished as prometaphase.

The mode of origin of the spindle varies considerably, but it is probably possible to reduce the essential details to a common plan. In the simplest cases it is formed (probably entirely out of nuclear sap after the dissolution of the membrane) as separate spindle elements corresponding in number to the chromosomes. This is the type of spindle found in the meiosis of some scale-insects [70] and in the female meiotic divisions of *Artemia salina*, the Brine Shrimp (Fig. 12).[59] Usually these spindle elements fuse completely to form a single gelatinous body in which the separate elements are no longer visible (Fig. 2c, d), but in the above cases they remain distinct, and do not even converge towards ' poles ' but end in fan-shaped expansions (Fig. 3a). In these and a number of other cases no trace can be found of centrosomes or asters, which leads one to the conclusion that, whatever their relation to the spindle when present, they are at any rate not essential to the division process. Where centrosomes and asters are present (as in the majority, but by no means all the Metazoa) an apparent spindle may form between them outside the nuclear membrane. In this case when the membrane disappears this structure (which is a good deal smaller than the final spindle and can be called the *central spindle*) moves into the middle of the nuclear area. The nuclear sap then apparently undergoes rapid gelation round the original central spindle so as to increase its volume considerably. Thus a compound spindle is formed which differs from the previous types only in having a central element not formed of nuclear sap but of extranuclear cytoplasm.[6]

The development of this central part of the spindle outside the nucleus in some cases has proved very confusing, since it has led to the conception of the chromosomes attaching themselves to a preformed spindle ; actually they are associated with the true spindle elements as soon as the latter are formed, and are probably never attached to the central element.

3. METAPHASE

At the end of prometaphase (the period in which the spindle is formed) the chromosomes are ' attached '—the term is misleading, but has to be retained—to the spindle in the region of the equator, that is to say equidistant from its two ends. The arrangement of the chromosomes at metaphase depends on a number of factors, (1) whether a central spindle element is present or not, (2) the number of the chromosomes and (3) their sizes. Where the chromosomes are very long or a large central element exists, as in the dividing leucocytes of Salamandra,[6] all the chromosomes are arranged round the periphery of the equator, irrespective of

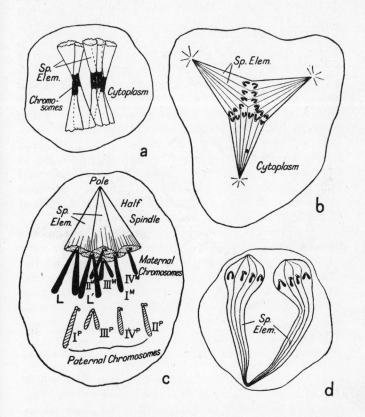

FIG. 3.—Various unusual types of spindles. a = the spindle
at the first meiotic division in the scale insect *Llaveia
bouvari* [70] where the spindle elements are quite separate.
b = a tripolar spindle at early anaphase. c = the half-
spindle formed at the first meiotic division in the fly
Sciara coprophila.[124] d = a late anaphase spindle in
a hybrid where the central region has undergone great
elongation.[41] In c all the maternal chromosomes
(including the two 'limited' ones L and L') go to the
pole, the paternal ones (I^P, II^P, III^P and IV^P in order
of size) moving in the opposite direction.

their number; their points of attachment are approximately equally spaced round the edge, so that if there are 6 chromosomes they will be 60° apart, if there are 24 (as in Salamandra) they will be 15° apart. Here it appears that the spindle elements associated with the chromosomes form a circle round the central element (Fig. 4a). In some organisms

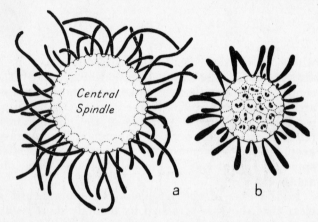

FIG. 4.—' Polar views ' of chromosomes and spindle at metaphase; *a* in the Salamander, where there are 24 large chromosomes which arrange themselves on the periphery, with a large central spindle element in the middle; *b* in an organism where there are 16 large chromosomes and 16 microchromosomes which arrange themselves in the centre of the spindle.

the two chromatids at this stage are strictly parallel, in others they wind round one another (cf. Fig. 5*b* and *i*).

Where there is no central element some of the chromosomes may be entirely embedded in the middle of the spindle. The following table shows the number which usually occupy the central region.[17]

These arrangements are found when all the chromosomes of the set are about the same size;

TABLE I

Total number of chromosomes	Number in the centre
Below 5	0
6	0–1
7–9	1
10	2
11–13	3
14	4–5
15	5
16	5–6
17–18	6
19	7

where there are considerable size-differences it is always the smaller chromosomes which occupy the centre of the spindle (Fig. 4b).* All these types of arrangement can be explained if the generalized repulsion between the surfaces of the chromosomes referred to earlier persists throughout metaphase, keeping the chromosomes with their associated spindle elements at a certain distance from one another.

In the case of the peripheral chromosomes it is clear that they are attached by a single short region to the spindle, so that their long arms float freely in the cytoplasm outside the spindle, perhaps covered by a layer of spindle-substance.[90] The region of attachment corresponds to one of the constrictions seen during prophase ; this constriction, the *spindle-attachment*, is thus a permanent cell-organ which, although visually similar to the other or *secondary constrictions*, behaves entirely differently. Although the smaller central chromosomes are usually entirely

* There are a few exceptions to this rule. The clearest case is that of the Tree Cricket *Oecanthus longicauda* [107] where the smaller chromosomes take up a peripheral position, with the larger ones in the centre. The same thing happens in many hybrids such as that between the moths *Biston hirtarius* and *Nyssia zonaria*, where the chromosomes of the two parent species are different in size and the large ones of *hirtarius* take up a central position in the hybrid.[26]

embedded in the substance of the spindle, they can be seen to have spindle attachments of exactly the same nature as the peripheral ones.

Where a chromosome has been broken into two parts as a result of irradiation by X-rays that part which contains the spindle attachment becomes associated with the developing spindle at prometaphase, while the part lacking a spindle attachment floats freely in the cytoplasm and never becomes attached to the spindle.[117, 180] There is thus some evidence for regarding the spindle attachment as the only part of the chromosome which plays a part in organizing the gelation of the spindle elements from the original nuclear sap ; perhaps ' spindle-element-organizer ' would be a clumsy but descriptive name for it.

The position of the spindle attachment is constant for each individual chromosome, but may vary from one chromosome to another in the set. Thus in *Drosophila melanogaster* (Fig. 20a) chromosomes I and IV have subterminal spindle attachments, while chromosomes II and III have median attachments. Where the attachment is median the chromosome will have the shape of a V with two limbs of equal length ; where it is submedian the two limbs will be unequal (Fig. 5). It was formerly believed that the spindle attachment was terminal in many cases and a distinction was drawn between ' V-shaped ' and ' rod-shaped ' chromosomes. It is now known that the attachment is never quite terminal ; in other words there are always two limbs to the V, only one may be so short as to be practically below the limit of optical resolution.[148, 180, 181]

In many cases of chromosomes with median or submedian spindle attachments there appears to be a minute granule in the centre of the spindle attachment which stains with aniline dyes and Haematoxylon ; it resembles the minute granule which forms the short limb of ' rod-shaped ' chromosomes.

DARLINGTON [36] regards this as the actual organ of attachment and calls it the ' attachment chromomere ' or ' centromere '. I have, however,[180] given reasons for believing that it is the non-staining region which is the true attachment-organ ; in many cases the ' centromere ' cannot be seen in the middle of the non-staining region, although it may be below the limit of visibility in these cases.

Apparently the spindle attachment, unlike the rest of the chromosome, remains undivided during prophase and only divides at prometaphase ; its two halves then organize a spindle element, above and below the equatorial plane. Up till now we have only been considering ordinary ' bipolar ' spindles ; but bipolarity is not an essential feature of the spindle—a fact which eliminates theories of mitosis based on a superficial analogy with electrical or magnetic models. In many cells such as those of cancerous tissues and in Sea-Urchin eggs which have been fertilized several times as a result of polyspermy, multipolar spindles with a number of equatorial planes intersecting one another are found [1, 10, 143] ; there may be as many as 12 poles and 6 equatorial planes. The probable structure of these multipolar spindles is indicated in Fig. 3b.

Even more interesting than the multipolar spindles are the unipolar ones (half-spindles) found at meiosis in some insects (Fig. 3c) and described by the SCHRADERS [71, 162] and by METZ, MOSES and HOPPE.[125] At present no useful suggestion can be put forward as to how they are formed.

So far we have said nothing of the ' spindle fibres ' described in many text-books, but have considered the spindle as a bundle of ' elements ' corresponding in number with the chromosomes, with or without the addition of a central element between the centrosomes. There appears to be little doubt that many of the ' continuous ' or ' interzonal ' fibres described by various workers were in fact fissures between the separate elements. On the other hand, this explanation cannot be put forward for the 'attachment fibres' connected with the chromosomes. These, however, have never been seen in living material and are invisible in well-fixed material in the majority of cases [10, 11, 152] ; they are most probably caused by shrinkage of the spindle in the fixing solution in those cases where they can be seen.[22] The term 'spindle fibre' should thus be dropped, at any rate until much more definite evidence is available ; whatever is the physical basis of the artefact it is not a *fibre* ; nor is the conception that 'spindle fibres' arise from 'lines of force' a useful one. If, as I believe, these structures arise from shrinkage of the spindle forming wrinkles or other longitudinal distortion-artefacts on the surface of the spindle elements it is only natural that these should be associated with any solid object such as the attachment point of a chromosome, which interrupts the substance of the spindle element. LEWIS and LEWIS [100] have shown that it is possible to produce 'spindle fibres' in living tissue-culture cells by the use of acid media ; the phenomenon is reversible, since on subsequently raising the pH the structures disappear.

We left the chromatids in prometaphase as a pair of thickened threads lying closely approximated throughout their length and only interrupted by the spindle attachment and the secondary constrictions (if any). Usually they come to lie even closer together at metaphase, so that the visible 'split' between them disappears ; a metaphase chromosome in transverse section thus has the shape of the symbol ∞. By most ordinary methods of fixation the metaphase chromatids show no trace of internal structure, but appear as homogeneous cylindrical rods (in some cases they are slightly club-shaped having a greater diameter at the distal ends than at the spindle attachment). By various special methods of fixation, however (fixing in boiling water,[156] squeezing the chromosomes under a cover-glass,[31] exposing them to fumes of ammonia or strong acids,[96, 98] it is possible to show that each chromatid has a spiral structure, the apparent cylinder being a spring in which the successive gyres are in contact (Fig. 2d). There is no doubt that this is the true structure in the living state ; all that the special methods of fixation have done is slightly to separate the gyres and thus reveal the spiral. The two chromatids are coiled independently (in other words their gyres do not interlock as happens when two parallel wires are wound round a cylinder) and in the same direction (right- or left-handed) at any one level ; the direction of coiling may change at the spindle attachment, but does not necessarily do so ; there is considerable doubt whether it may change direction elsewhere.[34, 73, 118, 137]

The existence of a spiral structure in metaphase chromosomes was discovered as early as 1880 by BARANETSKY and there seems no doubt that it is universally present both in plants and in animals.

The occurrence of a metaphase spiral explains the contract and condensation process during prophase ; this must now be interpreted as due to the development of the metaphase spiral. It will be remembered that in nuclei whose resting stage is of short duration, the early prophase chromosomes are also spiralized. We have therefore two kinds of spirals, those of early prophase and those which develop at the end of prophase and are completed by metaphase. The metaphase spirals are, however, not a continuation of the early prophase ones, since the latter have disappeared by mid-prophase ; as a matter of fact the reverse is the case ; that is to say, the early prophase spirals are the remains of the metaphase spirals of the *previous division* which have persisted through the intervening resting stage, and only finally unwind in the mid-prophase of the next

division if the resting stage is short (if it is protracted
they may completely unwind before the beginning
of prophase). DARLINGTON [34] calls the early prophase spirals *relic spirals* ; if in addition to the relic
spirals a larger spiral is present at early prophase,
he calls the larger one a *super spiral*, but both relic
and super spirals are due to the same cause, namely
unwinding of the previous metaphase spiral.

There are three ways in which the metaphase
spiral might develop during late prophase and prometaphase. There is, unfortunately, no direct evidence as to which of these actually occurs, since
observations on the origin of the metaphase spiral
are very incomplete, the internal structure of the
chromatids being difficult to study at this period.

According to the first method the chromosome
rotates in order to become spiralized (either one
end remains fixed and the other rotates or both
ends rotate in opposite directions or the spindle
attachment remains fixed and the ends rotate).
DARLINGTON [34] has given several reasons why this
cannot be the mode of origin of the metaphase spirals.
According to the second method an *internal compensating spiral* (whose twists are below the limit of
resolution of the microscope) develops in the opposite
direction to the main one (i.e. right-handed if the
main one is left-handed and vice versa) and with
the same number of turns as the main one. In
order to understand this internal compensating spiral
one can carry out a simple experiment with a piece
of copper wire : fix the two ends in a pair of vices
and wind the middle part into a spiral round a metal
rod : the compensating spiral will easily be seen.
DARLINGTON believes in the existence of this compensating spiral (which he calls the *molecular spiral*)
and regards it as causing the development of the
metaphase spiral. According to the third method
(which is possible in a colloidal body like a chromosome, but not in a piece of copper wire) there is no

internal compensating spiral ; a sliding of molecules on one another takes its place. It does not appear possible to decide at present which of the second and third alternatives is actually found in the chromosome.

FIRST STAGE OF ANAPHASE

Metaphase is a period during which almost no appreciable change takes place in the cell : it is nearly always one of the shortest stages of mitosis. At the end of metaphase the halves of the spindle attachments (the latter having divided at prometaphase) appear to repel one another. At any rate the proximal ends of the chromatids (those, that is to say, which are attached to the spindle) begin to diverge and to move up the sides of the spindle towards the poles (Fig. 2d). From the mode of travelling of the spindle attachments and in view of the fact that the spindle itself does not undergo any change of shape at this stage the hypothesis of an active repulsion between the divided spindle attachments is the only possible one. Certainly there is no evidence for a ' traction of fibres ' at this stage—the movement of the chromatids is autonomous and depends on the spindle attachments. Why this repulsion-force should not manifest itself earlier is not clear ; perhaps the division of the spindle attachments is not finally completed until the end of metaphase.

As a result of this movement of the chromatids the attachment regions of the latter move up the spindle towards the poles until in most cases they have travelled about two-thirds of the distance from the equator to the poles. Where the chromosomes are short this means that the split halves are now completely separated ; where they are long the distal ends (those farthest away from the spindle attachments) will be still in contact (Fig. 2e).

SECOND STAGE OF ANAPHASE

When the autonomous movement of the chromatids has come to an end a remarkable change in shape takes place in the spindle (Fig. 2e). Its middle region between the two groups of spindle attachments undergoes elongation so as to complete the separation of the two sets of chromatids (which must now be called chromosomes). The growth and elongation of the middle region of the spindle to form a *stem-body* is apparently a universal feature of mitosis [5]; unfortunately we have no idea what it is due to. The stem-body is clearly a solid gel like the rest of the spindle ; under abnormal conditions (e.g. in some hybrids and in cells cultured in hypertonic solutions) it may go on growing until the spindle is forced by lack of space to curl round in the cell (Fig. 3d). Usually the stem-body shows conspicuous longitudinal striations which are probably remnants of the divisions between the original spindle elements.

TELOPHASE

The two groups of ' daughter chromosomes ' never actually reach the poles of the spindle, although as a result of the elongation of the stem-body they may travel farther apart than the original distance between the poles of the metaphase spindle. When the cell has reached the stage represented by Fig. 2e the polar caps of the spindle disappear by a process of gel-solution ; the stem-body, on the other hand, frequently persists for a long time, even after cell division has been completed (Fig. 2f). As the polar caps of the spindle are destroyed a new nuclear membrane is formed round each of the telophase groups of chromosomes. The details of the process whereby the cytoplasm becomes divided into two daughter cells are outside the scope of this book.

The changes which take place inside the nuclear

membrane of the daughter nuclei during telophase are rather complicated but may briefly be described as a reversal of those which take place during the latter half of prophase—that is to say, de-condensation and de-spiralization. As a result of the latter the chromosomes become elongated and thrown into tight zig-zags inside the nuclear membrane. As they pass into the resting stage they become once more hydrated and lose their ' fixability '.

It will be remembered that we described the early prophase chromosomes as longitudinally split or divided into two chromatids. The telophase chromosomes, on the other hand, are unsplit and thus consist of a single chromatid each. The division of the chromosome in preparation for the next division thus takes place during the resting stage.*

The whole process of mitosis usually takes several hours from start to finish. From 2–24 hours is probably the usual range of variation in most organisms. In special cases, however (see Chap. I), it may take much longer. Prophase is nearly always the longest stage, prometaphase, metaphase and the two parts of anaphase are all short stages, while telophase is considerably longer, but usually not so long as prophase.

To sum up : mitosis consists of a series of cyclical colloidal phenomena, each of which is reversible. The main ones, so far as the chromosomes are concerned, are hydration, de-hydration, spiralization (condensation) and de-spiralization (de-condensation). Growth of the chromosome substance is probably an irreversible process and leads to the formation of two chromosome sets from what was originally a single

---

* There may be exceptions to this. Thus it appears that in anaphase and telophase of the second meiotic division in the plant *Tradescantia* the chromosomes are already split in preparation for the next division.[97] But in general the division of the chromosomes would appear to take place during the resting stage.[117, 180, 151]

set. The actual longitudinal division of the chromosomes takes place during the resting stage when they are invisible (or at any rate un-fixable), but the split halves (chromatids) remain closely approximated, due to the existence of a force of attraction between them, up to the beginning of anaphase. The formation of the spindle and the behaviour of the chromosomes at metaphase and anaphase depend on a special part of each chromosome, the spindle attachment, which persists throughout the mitotic cycle and is a self-perpetuating cell-organ with peculiar properties.

CHAPTER III

SPECIAL PROBLEMS OF MITOSIS

NUMBER, FORM AND SIZE OF CHROMOSOMES

THE number of chromosomes in the somatic nuclei of an organism is usually the same for all the tissues and for all the individuals of the same species. There are exceptions to both these statements (i.e. organisms with different chromosome numbers in different tissues and species with different chromosome numbers in different ' varieties '), but they need not be considered at present. The number of chromosomes in a somatic nucleus is usually even and is referred to as the *somatic number*. Where there are size-differences between the chromosomes of a somatic set it will usually be found possible to arrange them in pairs (Fig. 5), the two members of each pair being exactly alike in size, in position of spindle attachment and (where they exist) of secondary constrictions. The complete set of chromosomes is thus made up of two identical *haploid sets*. Organisms in which this is so are called *diploid organisms* and the somatic set may be called the *diploid set*. Sometimes even in diploid organisms one pair of chromosomes are unequal in size (Fig. 20) and sometimes the diploid number is uneven in one sex, there being a chromosome which does not form a member of a pair in that sex (Fig. 5*f*, *g*). In these cases the uneven pair or the odd chromosome are sex-chromosomes. Their behaviour will be considered later. In hybrids between species whose chromosome sets differ it is naturally not possible to arrange them in pairs since the two haploid sets in the hybrid are not identical.

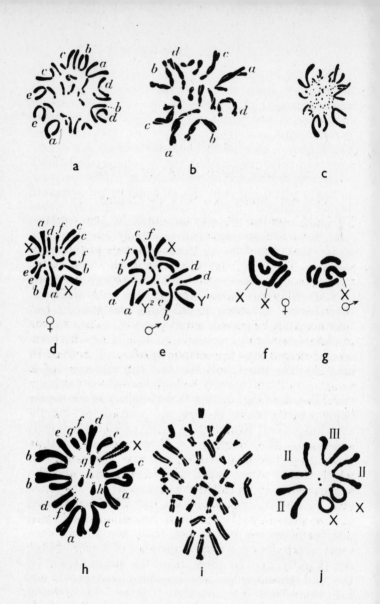

Fig. 5.

The two chromosomes of a pair are said to be *homologous*, since they contain the same series of genes arranged in the same order. The concept of homology is one which may be applied to parts of chromosomes as well as to whole ones, since one sometimes finds a pair of chromosomes which are homologous in some regions but not in others (see below).

In some organisms the chromosomes can be grouped, not into pairs, but into threes, fours or groupings of higher numbers. Such organisms (in which the somatic number is not diploid) are called *polyploids*, those with three of each kind of chromosome being *triploids*, those with four *tetraploids* and so on (pentaploids, hexaploids, heptaploids, octoploids, &c.).

The lowest diploid number found in any organism is 2, which occurs in the Roundworm, *Ascaris megalocephala* var. *univalens* (this species also has a tetraploid variety, *bivalens* with 4 chromosomes in the diploid set).* The highest diploid numbers hitherto recorded are 208 for a Crayfish [51] and a Crab [139] and 200 for the Great Water Dock (*Rumex hydro-*

---

* These numbers for the two varieties of *Ascaris megalocephala* refer only to the germinal tissues. In the somatic tissues a much larger number are found, as a result of fragmentation of the 2 or 4 originally present in the fertilized egg (see later).

FIG. 5.—Somatic chromosome sets of various organisms. *a* after MAKINO, [108] *b* after DARLINGTON, [36] *d* and *e* after YAMAMOTO, *f* and *g* after HUGHES SCHRADER, [70] *i* after MATSUURA and SUTO (*J. Fac. Sci.*, Hokkaido Imp. Univ. Ser., V, 5, 33), *j* after MORGAN, [127] the rest original. All figures slightly re-drawn. *b*, *d*, *e*, *i* are plants, the other organisms are animals. In *b* the coiling of the chromatids round one another is noticeable, in *i* the chromatids are parallel. The spindle attachments cannot be seen in *c*, *f*, and *g*, but are visible in all the others. In *a*, *c*, *f*, *g*, and *j* no trace of a 'split' between the chromatids can be seen, in the others it can be seen, either at the ends of the chromosomes, or throughout.

lapathum).[84]* Between these limits nearly all possible numbers are found in at least one species of animal or plant. Diploid numbers between 12 and 32 are common, those above and below these figures being progressively rarer. Both in animals and plants the commonest diploid number is 24 (Tables VIII and IX).

As regards size, the smallest known chromosomes are approximately 0·25 μ in length and about the same breadth at the metaphase of mitosis [177]; the longest ones are about 25 μ long and 2 μ in width.[3]

Normally each chromosome possesses only a single spindle attachment. By irradiation with X-rays it is, however, possible to cause two chromosomes to fuse in such a way that a compound chromosome is formed with two spindle attachments (Fig. 6a and b). Such a chromosome may behave in either of two ways at mitosis [117]; either both spindle attachments in each chromatid may go to the same pole at anaphase or to opposite poles (if those in one chromatid go to opposite poles, naturally those in the other will do likewise). When the spindle attachments in a chromatid go to opposite poles the part of the chromatid between them will be stretched out and eventually broken. Apparently each of the two ways of division happens in 50 per cent of cases ; the number of chromosomes with two spindle attachments is thus progressively reduced in the course of a few divisions, and such chromosomes stand no chance of becoming permanent.

One case exists, however, in which normal chromosomes have more than one spindle attachment each. That is in *Ascaris megalocephala* where the middle region of the long chromosomes found in the ' germ-line ' appears to contain about sixteen separate spindle attachments (Fig. 6c). Owing to the fact that these are very close together all those in one

* Some Protozoa (e.g. *Aggregata*) appear to have even more than this.

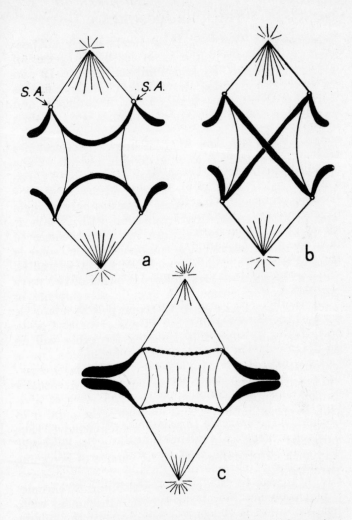

FIG. 6.—*a* and *b*: diagrams to show the two alternative modes of behaviour of a chromosome with two spindle attachments at anaphase; *c*: a diagram of the method of anaphase-separation in one of the germ-line chromosomes in *Ascaris megalocephala*; the numerous spindle attachments are situated so close together that those in one chromatid always go to the same pole.

chromatid are forced to go to the same pole at anaphase.[182] This happens in the spermatogonial and
oögonial divisions and at the first cleavage division.
In the later cleavage divisions, however, a different
type of division takes place in all those blastomeres
in which are going to give rise to the somatic tissues
of the adult—here the central region of the chromosomes breaks up into a number of much smaller
chromosomes, each of which probably has a single
spindle attachment. The ends of the chromosomes
are left with no spindle attachments and do not
become connected with the spindle in any way but
degenerate in the cytoplasm. This process results in
an organism whose germ-cells contain two or four
(according to the variety) large chromosomes, while
the somatic cells have a much larger number of small
chromosomes (the exact number of which is still in
doubt).

In another species of *Ascaris*, *A. lumbricoides*, the
ends of the chromosomes are broken off and degenerate in the cytoplasm in the same way, but there is
no fragmentation of the central region.[12]

Two other types of chromosomes may be mentioned here which have been observed on a number
of occasions, but do not appear to have become permanent in any wild species of organism. The first
of these is the *branched chromosome*. It was formerly
believed on genetical evidence that the '*pale*' mutation
of *Drosophila melanogaster* was due to a small piece
of the second chromosome having been broken off
and attached to the side of the third one. This
explanation has now been abandoned as far as the
pale mutation is concerned, but undoubted cases of
branched chromosomes have been seen in several
organisms.[27, 99] In most of these cases, the side-
branch was joined on to the main chromosome at
the spindle attachment.

The other type of chromosome is the *ring chromosome*, which has been found on a number of occasions,

both in normal cells (in which ring chromosomes have
apparently arisen spontaneously) and in X-rayed
material.[135, 103, 180] Here the two ends of the chromosome are fused together so that a closed ring results.
In *Drosophila melanogaster* there is a stock (the
' closed-X ' stock) in which the X-chromosome has
its proximal and distal ends fused so as to form a
ring.[127] In these cases the two rings which separate
from one another at anaphase may become inter-
locked like two links of a chain. This may lead to
both chromatids going to the same pole instead of
to opposite poles.

During prophase and metaphase the chromatids
of which the chromosome is composed are held together in a *paired* condition throughout their length
(Fig. 2). It appears (and observations on meiosis
confirm this) that they are held together, not merely
in a mechanical way (such as would result from a
common investing sheath—like two sausages in a
skin) but by a force of mutual attraction between the
homologous genes of which the chromatids are composed. Speculation as to the nature of this force is
outside the scope of this book ; but at the moment
it appears to be unparalleled in biological systems.
Now is this force exhausted when two chromatids
are in contact, in the paired condition, or does it
extend to other homologous chromatids (in other
words is the force exerted merely between pairs of
genes, or between threes and fours, &c.) ? In diploid
nuclei at prophase and metaphase each chromatid is
represented four times and if there was some ' residual ' attraction we should expect homologous
chromosomes to lie side by side in close approximation. Usually this is not the case, i.e. there is little
or no residual attraction, but it is exactly what does
happen in the two-winged flies (Diptera) including
Drosophila (Fig. 20) where the homologous chromosomes lie side by side (but not actually touching)
during prophase and metaphase. This state of

3

affairs is called *somatic pairing* ; there is apparently
sufficient residual attraction to cause it to develop
even in triploid nuclei (Fig. 20*b*). Apart from this
and a few other similar cases chromosomes always
keep at a certain distance from one another throughout the mitotic cycle as a result of the surface repulsion force already referred to.

GENETICALLY ACTIVE AND GENETICALLY INERT CHROMOSOMES

No attempt will be made here to explain how the
idea that the genes are arranged in linear order along
the chromatids has been proved, since the matter is
dealt with fully in all text-books of genetics. Certain
special problems must, however, be gone into. It has
long been known that the Y-chromosome in *Drosophila melanogaster* is genetically almost inactive.
Males lacking it (called X-nought males) are viable
but sterile. It has been shown that the Y contains
two separate genes necessary to ensure fertility in
addition to the normal allelomorph of the gene
' bobbed ' [168] ; apart from these it may contain a
few other genes. In Maize there is also a chromosome (the B-chromosome) which contains no known
genes and may be present any number of times in
the chromosome set or may be absent altogether
without in any way affecting the phenotypic appearance of the plant.[104] These, then, are examples of
inert chromosomes. It has recently been shown [131]
that the part of the X-chromosome in *D. melanogaster*
which is next to the spindle attachment (about one-
third of the total length) is almost completely inert
(up to the present this region only contains one known
gene, namely bobbed, which suggests that this region
is homologous with that part of the Y which likewise
contains bobbed). In addition there are almost
certainly small regions in the centre of chromosomes
II and III, on either side of the spindle attachment,
which are also inert. The possibility thus arises

that in many other organisms some chromosomes or regions of chromosomes may be genetically inert ; for this reason we must not expect the number of linkage groups and the haploid number of chromosomes to correspond in all cases.

SALIVARY GLAND CHROMOSOMES IN DIPTERA

In the nuclei of the salivary glands in the Diptera (and also in the nuclei of the rectal epithelium and the Malpighian tubules, which show an essentially identical structure) the chromosomes appear as enormously enlarged threads whose structure could not for a long time be interpreted in terms of ordinary mitotic chromosomes. The first clue to the analysis came when it was realized that in the salivary gland nuclei the phenomenon of somatic pairing is developed to the point where the homologous chromosomes are completely in contact throughout their length.[65] As a matter of fact it is often possible by means of crushing under a cover-glass to separate slightly the homologous chromosomes ; when this is done it will be seen that they are spirally wound round one another as in a piece of two-strand rope.[92] The number of these threads thus corresponds to the haploid, and not to the diploid number of chromosomes, but the two arms of V-shaped chromosomes are represented by separate threads ; thus in the female *Drosophila melanogaster* with eight chromosomes in the diploid set, four of which are V-shaped the salivary gland nuclei contain six threads (i.e. one representing the two X-chromosomes, one for each of the arms of the IInd and IIIrd chromosomes and a short one representing the two IVth chromosomes). In *Drosophila* all these six threads are attached at one end to a body called the *chromocentre*, to which the nucleolus is also attached by a thread, but in many other Diptera (e.g. *Bibio* and *Chironomus*) there is no chromocentre, the threads being separate and unconnected.[2, 65] Apparently the chromocentre results in part from a fusing together of the spindle attachments and adjacent regions of all the chromosomes.

The nuclei of the salivary gland cells are very large (about 25 μ in diameter in *Drosophila*) but even so the chromosomes are so long that they are tangled and coiled up so as to pack them inside the nuclear membrane. The usual method of studying these chromosomes consists in fixing and staining them simultaneously with a saturated solution of carmine in 40 per cent acetic acid to which a trace of an iron salt is added just before use. The preparations are then lightly crushed under a cover-glass in order to rupture the nuclear membranes and spread out the chromosomes on the slide. This crushing results in a considerable stretching of the chromosomes ; the X-chromosome of *D. melanogaster* may be 260 μ long, in acetocarmine preparations, while in the living salivary gland nucleus it is probably only about 150 μ in length. Even so the unstretched chromosomes in the salivary gland chromosomes are at least 50 times as long as the chromosomes at ordinary somatic mitoses and 1000 times their volume.

Each of the homologous chromosomes which pair to form the threads in the salivary gland nucleus is transversely striated with bands which stain with ordinary nuclear dyes (e.g. Crystal Violet and Haematoxylin). These cross bands are of varying thickness and are separated by non-staining internodes. It is apparently these internodes which stretch when the nucleus is crushed. The bands correspond exactly in position in the two homologous chromosomes and are always the same for a particular chromosome in different individuals of the same species. The thicker bands as seen in the uncrushed nuclei are apparently made up of several thinner bands which can be separated by crushing and stretching under a cover-glass. The total number of bands in the X-chromosome of *D. melanogaster* is at least

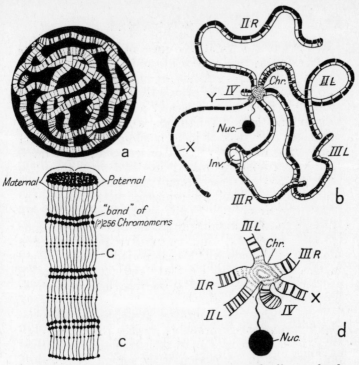

FIG. 7.—Diagrams illustrating the structure of salivary gland
chromosomes. *a* = a general view of a salivary gland
nucleus with the chromosomes coiled within it. The
' bands ' are shown, but not the threads connecting them.
The nuclear sap is shown in black. *b* = the chromosomes
of a salivary gland nucleus in the male *Drosophila
melanogaster* spread out by crushing the nucleus. The
maternal parts of the paired chromosomes are shown in
black, the paternal parts white. Chr. = chromocentre
(stippled) ; Nuc. = the nucleolus. II L and II R are
the two arms of the IInd chromosome, III L and III R the
two arms of the IIIrd chromosome ; the IVth chromosome and the X and Y chromosomes (the latter very small)
are also shown. An inversion (Inv.) is shown in the
' right ' arm of the IIIrd chromosome. *c* = a diagram of
a small part of a salivary gland chromosome, composed
of 256 threads, 128 paternal and 128 maternal. *d* = a diagram illustrating how the chromocentre is made up (in
the female of *D. melanogaster*) by a fusion of the inert
parts of all the chromosomes (represented by stippled
bands).

4,000 if one counts all the finer bands of which the thicker ones appear to be made up.[92]   Very frequently (but not always) the bands are in pairs, that is to say two adjacent ones are of exactly the same thickness (Fig. 6).   Each band is clearly a disk, that is to say they extend through the thickness of the chromosome ; moreover each disk or band is made up of a number of granules which have more or less completely fused to form a transverse plate ; in *Chironomus* there are at least 256 of these granules in each band.   The granules in one band are connected with those in the next by means of fine longitudinal threads which run through the non-staining internodes.   The two strands of our ' rope ' are thus themselves made up of a number of threads which bear periodic enlargements in the form of granules that tend (at any rate in acetocarmine preparations) to fuse into transverse bands.[19, 92, 95]

This interpretation of the structure of salivary gland chromosomes probably applies to all Diptera ; various other theories as to their structure have been put forward in connexion with genera (*Drosophila* and *Sciara*) whose salivary gland chromosomes do not appear to fix very satisfactorily in acetocarmine ; but in larvae of midges (*Chironomidae*) there can be no doubt that the above is the correct interpretation.

The salivary gland chromosomes are thus to be regarded as resting stage or early prophase chromatids stretched out straight which are not wound into a tight spiral as at an ordinary somatic metaphase and which have split longitudinally again and again.   All the peculiarities of the salivary gland nuclei can be explained on the basis of these two simple assumptions if one takes into account the well-known somatic pairing phenomenon found in all Diptera.   The fact that the salivary gland chromosomes are about fifty times the length of the ordinary metaphase chromosomes will be understood if one takes a tightly coiled spring and pulls it out straight.   The great volume of the salivary gland nuclei (about 65,000 μ [3]) is natural if they are polyploid and the thickness of the chromosomes results from the fact that they have divided a large number of times.

The formation of the chromocentre has recently been shown [149] to be due to the fact that the regions immediately adjace ntto the spindle attachment (which are inert but all ' homologous ') have, as a result of their homology, all fused into a single mass (Fig. 7d). The origin of the chromocentre is thus ultimately the result of the somatic pairing phenomenon. Diptera which lack a chromocentre presumably lack the homologous regions next to the spindle attachments.

SEX-CHROMOSOMES

All chromosomes other than sex-chromosomes are called *autosomes*. The sex-determining mechanism of the majority of bisexual animals and plants consists of a pair of chromosomes which may be regarded as modified autosomes. In one sex these form an equal pair of homologous chromosomes while in the other the pair is unequal. The sex which possesses the unequal pair is called the *heterogametic sex* since it produces two kinds of gametes or spores ; the other sex is called the *homogametic sex*. In most groups of organisms it is the male which is the heterogametic sex (that is to say there are two kinds of sperms or pollen grains and only one kind of egg or megaspore), but in some groups it is the female which is heterogametic—that is to say there are two kinds of eggs or megaspores, all the sperms or pollen grains being alike (see Table II). In the Bryophyta (mosses and liverworts) where the sexual stage of the life cycle is haploid the male and female gametophytes each contain one member of a pair of sex-chromosomes.

It will be seen that the sex-determining mechanism is merely a special kind of heterozygosity—in respect of a whole chromosome instead of in respect of a

single gene. The sex-chromosomes are in most cases
(perhaps in all) not the only ones bearing sex-determining genes ; probably all the autosomes carry
genes which are concerned with the development
of characters of one or the other sex ; all that the sex-
chromosomes do is to act as a differential mechanism
which switches the development of the embryo over
to maleness or femaleness from a potentially hermaphrodite condition.

According to the usual terminology the chromosomes forming the equal pair in the homogametic
sex are called X-chromosomes. The diploid set in
the heterogametic sex contains one X-chromosome
and in addition a chromosome bearing a greater or
less resemblance to it called the Y-chromosome. We
can regard the various types of sex-chromosomes as
progressive evolutionary modifications of an original
pair of autosomes, these modifications consisting of
the XY pair becoming more and more unlike. In the
majority of fishes and amphibia there is no visible
cytological difference between the X and the Y ; they
probably only differ in respect of a few genes. Thus
in fishes of the genus Platypoecilus one species has
male heterogamety, another female heterogamety.[8]
In most mammals and in many insects (such as
Drosophila melanogaster) the X and the Y are of
very different sizes so that they can easily be distinguished. Here it is probable that only a short
region of the Y is homologous to a similar short
region in the X. Usually the Y is smaller than the
X but in some cases, as in *D. melanogaster* it is considerably longer. In many organisms the Y is very
small indeed and in a large number of groups it has
been lost altogether. In these the diploid set in the
heterogametic sex consists of an odd number of
chromosomes (one less than in the homogametic
sex).

In a number of organisms the X is represented by
two separate chromosomes which can be called X^1

and X^2. Thus in the Praying Mantis the chromosome sets of the two sexes are:

Male   13 pairs of autosomes, X^1, X^2, Y
Female 13   ,,   ,, X^1, X^1, X^2, X^2.

In this case it will be seen that the heterogametic sex has an odd number of chromosomes, but a Y is present.[88] The two ends of the Y are probably homologous to regions in the X^1 and X^2 respectively (Fig. 8b).

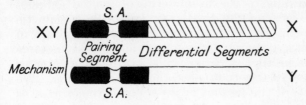

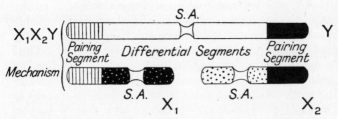

FIG. 8.—Diagrams of the sex-chromosomes (above) the male rat, and (below) the male Praying Mantis. The homologies of the various regions are indicated diagrammatically. S.A. = spindle attachment.

In the insect *Perla marginata*[80] there is a similar situation but a Y is absent so that the two sets are:

Male   10 pairs of autosomes, X^1, X^2
Female 10   ,,   ,, X^1, X^1, X^2, X^2.

In some cases it is the Y which is represented by two separate chromosomes, there being only one X. Thus in the dioecious Sorrel Dock, *Rumex acetosa*, we have:

Male plant   6 pairs of autosomes, X, Y[1], Y[2]
Female plant 6   ,,   ,,   X, X.

In this case it will be seen that the heterogametic sex possesses one more chromosome than the other instead of one less as in the XX : X type.[190]

TABLE II

MALE HETEROGAMETIC AND FEMALE HOMOGAMETIC.	FEMALE HETEROGAMETIC AND MALE HOMOGAMETIC.
Animals	
All Insects except . .	those with haploid males and the Lepidoptera and Trichoptera [165, 89]
Crustacea Arachnida Opisthogoneata Annelida Nematoda Echinodermata (as far as known)	} [161]
All Vertebrates except . .	Some Fishes [8] Some Reptiles at any rate [140] All Birds [177, 167]
Plants [161]	
Rumex section Acetosa	Hexaploid *Fragaria elatior* [101]
Humulus Melandrium Populus Empetrum Elodea	

TABLE III

ORGANISMS WITH SEX-DETERMINATION BY MALE HAPLOIDY
Insects : *Rhynchota*

Some Aleurodidae [171]
Some Coccidae [162, 69]
Hymenoptera
Probably all [157, 172, 134]
Coleoptera : Micromalthus debilis [164]
Arachnida : *Acarina* (Mites)
Some at least [160, 146]
Rotifera : *Aslanchna* [184]
(Also possibly in some *Thysanoptera*)

The identification of sex-chromosomes is naturally difficult when the X and Y are cytologically indistinguishable. Where they are visibly different it is usually possible to identify them by careful comparison between the somatic chromosome sets of the two sexes. In the more highly evolved types of sex-determining mechanism the sex-chromosomes, or at any rate parts of them, are often clearly recognizable by the fact that they contract during prophase at a different rate to the autosomes (usually slower). Thus in the spermatogonial mitoses of the Acrididae and Gryllidae (Grasshoppers and Crickets) the greater part of the X has only reached the mid-prophase degree of contraction by the time the autosomes are in metaphase.[141, 180] This process of differential condensation is known as *heteropycnosis*. In the above case we can speak of *negative heteropycnosis* ; the opposite condition of *positive heteropycnosis* (where the sex-chromosome reaches the metaphase degree of contraction when the autosomes are still in early prophase) is often found in the first meiotic division (see Chap. 5).[7, 38]

Heteropycnosis is not confined to sex-chromosomes ; thus in many species of grasshoppers there is one autosome which shows strong positive heteropycnosis in about two-thirds of its length at the first meiotic division.[18] Moreover in *Drosophila melanogaster* all the inert regions show heteropycnosis at the somatic divisions. There seems to be some sort of connexion between inertness and heteropycnosis, but it is not possible as yet to state definitely that all heteropycnotic regions are more or less inert and vice versa.

In a number of groups of organisms sex-determination does not depend on a pair of sex-chromosomes, but on whether the eggs are fertilized or develop parthenogenetically. Thus in these cases the males are haploid, the females diploid. This is the case in the Hymenoptera, the Mites (some species at any rate) and in some Scale Insects (Coccidae). In the Hymenoptera

it is clear from recent work on the parasitic wasp
Habrobracon that the haploid-diploid scheme of sex-
determination co-exists with a mechanism involving
female heterogamety.[172]   The females possess an X-
and a Y-chromosome and thus produce two kinds
of eggs, X-eggs and Y-eggs.   If these develop without fertilization they give rise to haploid males which
are accordingly of two types, X-males and Y-males.
These produce sperms by a modified meiosis which
does not involve any reduction in number of chromosomes.   Normally X-eggs are only fertilized by Y
sperms and vice versa, giving rise to diploid XY-
females ;   occasionally, however, X-sperms fertilize
X-eggs and Y-sperms Y-eggs.   The result of this is
to produce extremely rare diploid male individuals.
Femaleness in Habrobracon clearly depends on an
interaction of genes present in the X- and Y-chromosomes ;   which explains why both haploid and homozygous individuals are males.

POLYPLOIDY

Polyploid cells arise in the first place through a
failure of cell division ;   that is to say that in a particular cell the chromosomes divide, but the cell fails
to do so.[178, 179]   If this happens in a diploid organism
a tetraploid cell will result.   Such a process occurs
normally in a small percentage of the meristem cells
in the root tips of certain plants [121, 126] ;   as a result
patches of tetraploid tissue are produced, surrounded
by diploid cells.   In the tomato it is possible to produce tetraploid shoots by repeated cutting back.[79]
From such shoots it is possible to produce tetraploid
tomato plants.

If the process is repeated in a tetraploid plant
octoploid cells will be produced.   Triploids arise in
the main through crossing between diploids and tetraploids, hexaploids by a doubling of the chromosome
set in a triploid and pentaploids by crossing between
tetraploids and hexaploids.

It has been found necessary to distinguish between two kinds of polyploidy which are called *auto-polyploidy* and *allo-polyploidy*. An auto-polyploid is an organism with more than two haploid sets of chromosomes which are all alike—it has arisen by doubling of the chromosomes in an individual which is not a hybrid. In an allo-polyploid, on the other hand, the doubling has taken place in a hybrid, so that the several haploid sets are not all identical, having been derived from different parent species.

Polyploidy may occur within a single species, as in the case of the Cruciferous plant *Biscutella laevigata* where diploid, triploid, tetraploid, pentaploid and hexaploid plants have been found [112] or as between different species of the same genus. A good example of the latter phenomenon is the Section Lapathum of the genus *Rumex* (Table V). Intraspecific polyploidy is of course always auto-polyploidy, while the interspecific kind may be either auto- or allo-polyploidy.

A special type of polyploidy occurs where one or more chromosomes, but not the whole haploid set, are present more than twice in the complete chromosome set ; this is called *polysomy*. The most common type of polysomy is *trisomy* where one or more chromosomes are present three times, the others being only present twice. The opposite phenomenon where a polyploid lacks one or more chromosomes from one

TABLE IV

If n = the haploid number of one species and n that of another, then—

2n = diploid number of first species
$2n$ =   ,,   ,,   ,, second species
n + n = diploid number of hybrid between them
3n and $3n$ = the auto-triploids
4n and $4n$ = the auto-tetraploids
2n + $2n$ = the allo-tetraploid
2n + 1 = a trisomic } these terms are partially inter-
4n − 1 = an aneuploid }   changeable
4n + $2n$ and 3n + $3n$ = different kinds of allo-hexaploids

haploid set is called *aneuploidy* : it is obvious that
there is no hard and fast distinction between polysomy
and aneuploidy (see Table IV).

TABLE V

SOMATIC CHROMOSOME NUMBERS IN THE GENUS RUMEX
(SECTION LAPATHUM) [84], [77], [78]

R. salicifolius	20
R. alpinus	20
R. obtusifolius (one var.) . . .	20
R. conglomeratus.	20
R. sanguineus	20
R. scutatus	20
R. pulcher (one var.) . . .	20
R. maritimus	40
R. limosus	40
R. brittanicus (one var.) . . .	40
R. pulcher (another var.) . . .	40
R. domesticus	40
R. obtusifolius (another var.) . .	40
R. crispus	60
R. patientia	60
R. orientalis	60
R. domesticus (another var.) . .	60
,, (,, ,,) . .	80
R. japonicus	100
R. hymenosepalus	100
R. andraeanus	120
R. brittanicus (another var.) . .	160
R. aquaticus	200
R. hydrolapathum	200

Owing to the fact that in bisexual organisms the
sex-determining mechanism depends in general on
the segregation of a single pair of chromosomes at
meiosis polyploid species and varieties are usually
found only in groups where reproduction does not
depend on bisexuality (most Angiosperms, parthenogenetic and hermaphrodite animals such as the
Pulmonata, Oligochaeta, &c.). If polyploidy occurred
in bisexual species it would completely upset the
sex-determining mechanism.[130] Since the vast majority of Angiosperms are monoecious while the bulk
of the Metazoa are dioecious polyploidy is far commoner in the higher plants than in animals.

CHAPTER IV

THE GENERAL OUTLINE OF MEIOSIS

MEIOSIS is the antithesis of fertilization ; in diploid organisms it results in the chromosomes being reduced to the haploid number. If meiosis takes place at the beginning of the life-cycle, just after fertilization (this type of meiosis is called *initial* or *zygotic meiosis* and occurs in most of the Sporozoa and in the Charices,[50] Basidiomycetes [15] and Ascomycetes [189] among plants as well as in some of the lower Algae [63]) the synthesis (to use a philosophical term) of fertilization and meiosis will be a haploid adult organism. If on the other hand meiosis occurs just before fertilization (i.e. during gamete formation) as happens in all the higher animals (Metazoa) then the adult organism will be diploid. In the higher plants with an alternation between the sporophyte and gametophyte generation meiosis takes place during spore-formation, i.e. occupies an intermediate place in the life-cycle ; where the gametophyte generation is the predominant one (as in the mosses and liverworts) the ' adult ' phase of the life-cycle will be haploid ; where it is the sporophyte which is predominant (as in the Pteridophytes and Phanerogams) the ' adult ' phase will be diploid. Thus a moss-plant is haploid and a buttercup diploid, but in both meiosis takes place at the same stage in the life-cycle, during spore-formation.

Meiosis has been defined by DARLINGTON [31] as ' the occurrence of two divisions of a nucleus accompanied by one division of its chromosomes '. The whole process must be regarded as having arisen in the

47

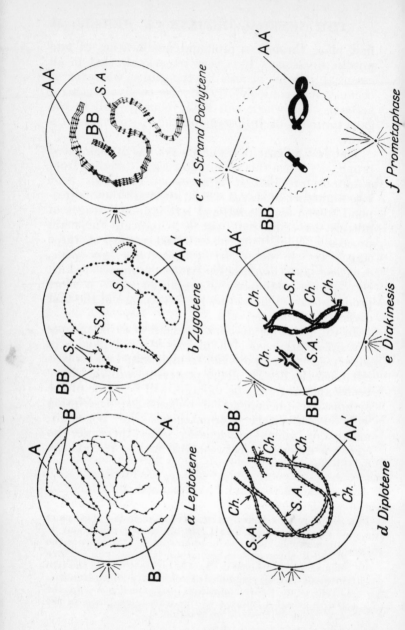

a Leptotene

b Zygotene

c 4-Strand Pachytene

d Diplotene

e Diakinesis

f Prometaphase

first place through a profound modification of two mitotic divisions. It is very remarkable that in all essential details meiosis is the same wherever it occurs ; it is consequently possible to give a general account of it which will apply equally well to the gametogenesis of an insect and the sporogenesis of a plant.

The first meiotic division always has an elongated prophase ; since this is in many ways different from a mitotic prophase it is necessary to subdivide it into a number of stages which, although they correspond to the early, mid- and late prophase stages of mitosis, have different names to indicate the main processes which take place. The names of these stages are, in order, *leptotene, zygotene, pachytene, diplotene* and *diakinesis*. After diakinesis (which corresponds to the end of prophase) comes a short prometaphase, followed by the metaphase of the first division (' First Metaphase ').

In the following account we shall describe meiosis in a diploid organism ; the meiosis of a polyploid is in some respects more difficult to understand and is best left until the details of the process in a diploid have been explained. As no mention will be made of the cytoplasmic phenomena of meiosis the description will do for either spermatogenesis or oogenesis, macro- or micro-sporogenesis, since there are no constant differences between the nuclear phenomena in the two sexes.

FIG. 9.—Diagrams of the main stages of meiosis. Two pairs of chromosomes AA′ and BB′ are shown, the A and A′ chromosomes having submedian spindle attachments, the B and B′ chromosomes having sub-terminal ones. Three chiasmata are formed in the AA′ bivalent, one in the BB′ bivalent. S.A. = spindle attachment, Ch. = chiasma. There is no " terminalization " of chiasmata. In the BB′ bivalent a rotation of the arms takes place, in the AA′ bivalent there is no rotation.

4

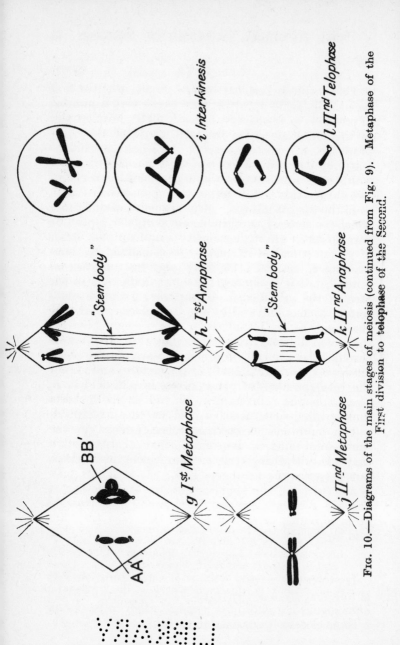

FIG. 10.—Diagrams of the main stages of meiosis (continued from Fig. 9). Metaphase of the First division to telophase of the Second.

LEPTOTENE

This is the earliest part of the prophase of the first meiotic division—it corresponds to the very beginning of prophase in an ordinary mitosis. The chromosomes in the leptotene stage resemble those of the early prophase of mitosis except for one important feature ; *they are not longitudinally divided*—in other words each consists of a single chromatid and not of two chromatids held together throughout their length as in the case of mitosis. Another point of difference which is somewhat variable is that the leptotene chromosomes are rather clearly made up of a series of granules (called *chromomeres*) connected by non-staining intervals ; this may also be the case at mitosis, but it is not usually so obvious. As in the case of the granules in the salivary gland chromosomes it has naturally been suggested that the chromomeres are actual genes. In various *Liliaceae* the total number of chromomeres in the whole chromosome set has been counted and found to lie between 1,500 and 2,500 [9] ; of course we do not know the total number of genes in these plants, but in *Drosophila* the total number (including the hitherto undiscovered ones) has been estimated at 14,000.[56]

The leptotene chromosomes are present in the same number as in the somatic tissues ; very often they are not arranged at random inside the nucleus, but preserve the arrangement of the previous telephase (with all the spindle attachments together at one side of the nucleus and the chromosomes arranged as in a bunch of flowers [76] ; in this case they are said to be polarized.

ZYGOTENE

Leptotene is usually a stage of short duration. It is followed by a stage called zygotene in which the homologous chromosomes come together in pairs and become closely approximated throughout their length.

This process is called *pairing* or (in the older accounts) *synapsis*. In the case of each pair of homologous chromosomes the pairing process begins at one or more points and then spreads along the length of the chromosomes (Fig. 9b). Where the telophase arrangement of the previous division has been retained pairing begins at the spindle attachments—otherwise it may begin anywhere. It must be pointed out that the pairing is not merely between homologous chromosomes, but always between strictly homologous regions ; this can be seen very clearly where the chromomeres are distinct, since they are of slightly different sizes (Fig. 9b). If we call those in one homologous chromosome a, b, c, d, . . . and those in the other a', b', c', d', . . . then a will pair with a' and b with b' and so on. If a short region has become inverted in one homologous chromosome but not in the other (as sometimes happens) then the inverted region will remain as an unpaired loop in the middle (Fig. 11a). If a rather longer section is inverted the loop will twist round and pair as in Fig. 11b. If a small section is completely missing from one chromosome, then the corresponding section in the homologous chromosome will form a short loop (Fig. 11c).[31] It appears, therefore, that the force of attraction is a mutual one between homologous chromomeres (or genes) and that it is probably identical with the force which keeps the two chromatids of a chromosome together throughout their length in the prophase of mitosis. It seems natural that this force should lead to a pairing of homologous chromosomes at zygotene, since these have not undergone the usual longitudinal division—they are still unsplit at a stage when they would normally be split ; the force of attraction thus satisfies itself at mitosis by maintaining chromatids together and at zygotene by bringing distinct chromosomes into longitudinal approximation.[154] DARLINGTON regards the prophase of the first meiotic division as ' precocious ' in

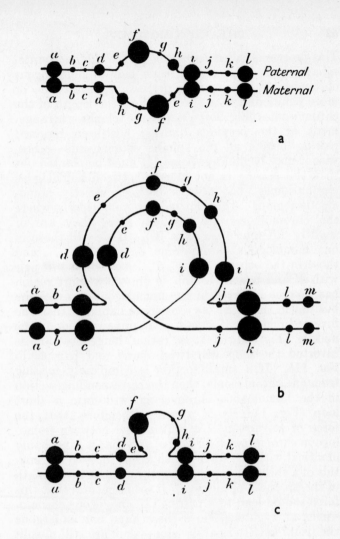

Fig. 11.—Diagrams of chromomeres (or genes) at the two-strand pachytene stage in a bivalent which is heterozygous for (a) a small inversion, (b) a large inversion, (c) a deletion.

comparison with the prophase of an ordinary mitosis, but it is probably better to regard the splitting of the chromosomes as being delayed.

PACHYTENE

As a result of pairing the apparent number of chromosome threads (in a diploid organism) has been reduced to half; if there were $2n$ chromosomes in leptotene there will be n associations of two chromosomes at the beginning of pachytene. These associations of pairs of chromosomes are called *bivalents*. Each bivalent has a split down the middle and thus closely simulates an ordinary mitotic chromosome at

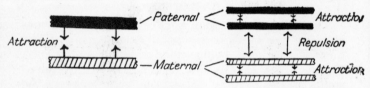

FIG. 12.—Diagrams to show how the attraction between homologous chromosomes *before* they have split becomes converted into a repulsion as soon as splitting has occurred.

mid-prophase, although it has arisen in a totally different way, by pairing of two entirely distinct chromosomes instead of by splitting of a single one. Another important point of difference is that the pachytene bivalent has two distinct spindle attachment points, whereas the mitotic prophase chromosome has only one which does not divide until prometaphase.

Naturally the double pachytene threads are twice as thick as the single leptotene threads; they are also a good deal shorter since contraction takes place during zygotene.

Half-way through pachytene the splitting which at mitosis has occurred before the beginning of prophase takes place. Thus the division process is not suppressed in the first meiotic division, it is merely postponed until a stage which corresponds to about half-way through prophase. Pachytene can thus be subdivided into a two-strand stage (before splitting), and a four-strand stage (after splitting).

At the beginning of pachytene the two threads are lying strictly parallel, but they soon begin to wind round one another like the two wires of a piece of electric flex ; thus when splitting takes place it results in four threads two of which are wound round the other two. The reason for this coiling is not quite clear, but it is possibly accompanied by a slight increase in length of the threads.[33]

DIPLOTENE

The force of attraction between homologous genes seems in general to be restricted to two genes at any one level, there being no ' residual attraction '. That is to say that as soon as the pachytene chromosomes have split the attraction force between the paternal and maternal chromosomes ceases to exist, being replaced by an attraction between the two chromatids of which each chromosome is composed (Fig. 12). In this respect the pachytene chromosome resembles an ordinary mitotic chromosome and differs from a salivary gland chromosome in which as many as 256 chromomeres mutually attract one another in each transverse ' band ' (page 38). As a result of the disappearance of the attraction force between the chromosomes these begin to separate, being repelled by the surface repulsion force which is a general property of all chromosomes, but which has been overcome in zygotene and pachytene by the pairing attraction-force. The moment when the two homologous chromosomes begin to separate marks the transition from pachytene to diplotene. If they were to separate completely we should have another stage similar to leptotene ; actually, however, they do not do so but remain held together at certain points (called *chiasmata*). If one of those chiasmata is examined it will be seen that two out of the four chromatids at this point form an X (Fig. 9*d*). These chiasmata were seen as early as 1893 [154] and are now known to be an almost universal feature of the diplotene and later stages in all organisms (certain exceptions will be mentioned in the next chapter). There is always (apart from very rare cases) at least one chiasma in each bivalent and there may be as many as twelve (in the long bivalent of the broad-bean, *Vicia Faba* [106]). As soon as the phenomenon of genetical crossing-over was discovered it was naturally suggested that the chiasmata formed the physical basis of crossing-over.

The average number of chiasmata in a bivalent is known as the *chiasma-frequency*. One can speak of the chiasma-frequency of a particular bivalent or of the whole chromosome set in an organism. The former varies from 1·0 to about 8·56 (in the long bivalent of the domestic chicken [183]). The genetical significance of chiasma-frequencies is dealt with in the next chapter. The appearance of bivalents with one and three chiasmata respectively is shown in Fig. 9*d* and *e*. A bivalent with a single chiasma about half-way along its length forms a four-armed structure while in the case of a bivalent with several chiasmata there are a series of loops between the chiasmata. It is important to distinguish between true chiasmata and places where one chromosome of which the bivalent is composed merely passes over or under the other.[33] The difference between these two is shown in Fig. 9*d* ; in actual material it is generally quite easy to tell them apart by careful focusing up and down.

There are two possible ways of interpreting chiasmata (Fig. 13), and for a long time it was uncertain which was correct. On the first hypothesis no breaking of chromatids has taken place before the appearance of the chiasmata, and the four threads are

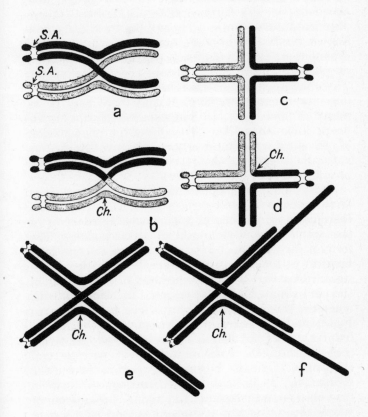

FIG. 13.—Diagrams to illustrate the difference between the
old and the modern theory of chiasma-formation.
Maternal chromosome black, paternal one stippled (or
vice versa). *a*, an equal bivalent with a single chiasma
on the old theory ; *b*, the same on the new theory,
c, the same bivalent on the old theory after rotation,
d, on the new theory after rotation. *e* and *f* provide
the proof that the new theory is the correct one. *e* is an
unequal bivalent with a single chiasma as actually found,
f is what would happen in such a bivalent if the old
theory were true (never found).

consequently unaltered ; on this hypothesis a paternal and a maternal chromatid actually ' cross over ' (in the literal sense) in such a way that on one side of the chiasma a paternal chromatid is paired with a paternal and a maternal with a maternal while on the other side a paternal is paired with a maternal, and a maternal with a paternal.

On the second hypothesis two of the four chromatids have broken at the end of pachytene at exactly the same level and re-joined diagonally in such a way as to produce an X (Fig. 13*b*). On the first hypothesis a chiasma *may* give rise (by subsequent breaking) to a genetical cross-over ; on the second hypothesis a genetical cross-over (breakage and reciprocal re-fusion) has preceded the appearance of the chiasma and given rise to it. On the second hypothesis a paternal chromatid is associated with another paternal one and a maternal with another maternal one on *either* side of the chiasma. It is now known with complete certainty that the second hypothesis is the correct one. There are a number of proofs but the simplest one is given in Fig. 13*e* and *f*. It sometimes happens that there is an unequal pair of chromosomes (i.e. a piece has been broken off the end of either the paternal or the maternal one, so that the genes that they contain are, e.g. *abcdefghijklmn* and *abcdefghi*). In this case if a single chiasma is formed in the a . . . i region the result will be an ' unequal bivalent ' as in Fig. 13*e* and not as in Fig. 13*f*.[176] This is quite a conclusive proof of the second hypothesis ; there are others which are even more conclusive but more difficult to understand.[28, 37, 115]

Each chiasma is thus a visible sign that a single genetical cross-over has taken place. We have now to ask what is it that causes the chromatids to break, why do a paternal one and a maternal one always break at the same level, why do never more nor less than two break at that level and, finally, why does reciprocal re-fusion always take place ? Entirely

satisfactory answers to all these questions cannot be
given as yet, but a series of preliminary hypotheses
have been put forward [33]; it seems certain that the
initial breakage relieves a localized strain as the
spirally twisted chromosomes separate. It is clear
that the moment of breakage is *after* the chromosomes
have split and *before* they have separated, i.e. in the
very short four-strand pachytene stage.

Once the loops between the chiasmata have opened
out (as a result of the repulsion mentioned above) and
the diplotene bivalents have acquired their characteristic appearance (Fig. 9d) three kinds of changes
begin to take place in the bivalents : the first two of
these are universally found, while the third occurs
in many organisms but not in all.

The first change is a shortening and thickening of
the chromatid threads ; this can easily be seen by
comparing Fig. 9d and e. It probably takes place
in exactly the same way as the contraction of mitotic
chromosomes between mid- and late prophase. (See
Chap. II, p. 12.)

The second change is most marked in bivalents
with a single chiasma and consists of a relative rotation of two arms of the cross through about 180°
(relative to the other two arms). The result is that
a bivalent with a single chiasma which looks
like Fig. 13b at early diplotene comes to look
like Fig. 13d at late diplotene. In the case of
bivalents with several chiasmata the rotation is
usually through only about 90°—thus the successive
loops between the chiasmata come to lie in planes at
right-angles to one another, the alternate ones lying
in the same plane. The appearance of the bivalent
is similar to that of a chain stretched out tight.

The third change consists of an actual moving of
the chiasmata towards the ends of the chromosomes.
This is shown in Fig. 14a, b and c, which represent
successive stages in the process. Of course the point
where the paternal and maternal portions of the

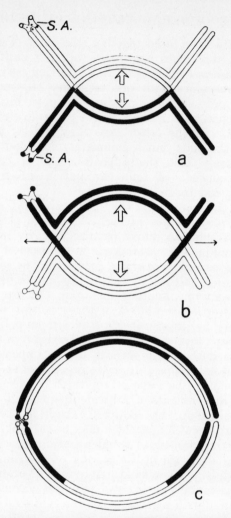

Fig. 14.—Diagrams to show terminalization of two chiasmata in a bivalent with quasi-terminal spindle attachments. *a*, the bivalent at early diplotene when the chiasmata correspond in position to the points of crossing-over; *b*, at late diplotene; *c*, at diakinesis when terminalization is completed. The hollow arrows represent the force of repulsion inside the loop, the solid arrows the direction in which the chiasmata are moving.

chromatid have fused together (the point of genetical crossing-over) does not move—all that shifts is the *visible chiasma*. This process of shifting may happen in chromosomes with one or many chiasmata ; it may be only slight or may result (as in Fig. 14c) in all the chiasmata moving to the extreme ends of the bivalent. In the latter case they appear never to slip off the ends, but a completely terminal chiasma has entirely lost the appearance of a cross ; it merely consists of four chromatids which are in contact, end to end (Fig. 14c).[31, 36]

Both the second and the third processes ('*rotation*' and '*terminalization*') clearly depend in part on the general repulsion force (represented by a hollow arrow in Fig. 14). This leads in the case of rotation to the loops and '*free arms*' (which may be considered as forming half-loops) taking up positions farther away from one another in space. In the case of terminalization the effect of the repulsion force will obviously be greater inside a closed loop than in a '*half-loop*' and will lead to an expansion of the loop, or loops if there are several, at the expense of the terminal half-loops. In some organisms at any rate there seems to be a special repulsion between the two spindle attachments of a bivalent so that if these lie in a closed loop, that loop will expand at the expense of any adjacent loops which may be present. Naturally as this process of terminalization takes place it involves a change in the pairing relationships of the chromatids. Whereas at first, points of crossing-over and chiasmata coincide and paternal chromatids are only paired with paternal, and maternal with maternal (Fig. 14a), as they diverge paternal and maternal chromatids come to lie paired for a certain distance (between the point of crossing-over and the new position of the chiasma). This shows that it is not a failure of the paternal and maternal chromatids to attract one another which prevents them remaining paired after the split has occurred in pachytene—the reason why they separate after splitting is probably merely that the two paternal threads are farther away from the two maternal ones than they are from one another.

DIAKINESIS

This-stage corresponds to the late prophase of an ordinary mitotic division. Diplotene passes quite gradually into diakinesis so that it is quite impossible to say when one ends and the other begins. There is much to be said for abolishing the term diakinesis altogether and substituting 'late diplotene' for it. The most noticeable difference between the bivalents in diakinesis and diplotene is that they have become much thicker and shorter in diakinesis. As a result of the thickening of the chromatids the split between them becomes more difficult to see—in many cases it becomes quite invisible by the end of diakinesis (it will be remembered that a similar phenomenon takes place at mitosis). 'Rotation' is usually completed by the beginning of diakinesis but 'terminalization' may continue right up to the metaphase of the first meiotic division.

As in the late prophase of mitosis there is in diakinesis a strong tendency for the thickened chromosomes to move to the periphery of the nucleus and to arrange themselves on the inside of the nuclear membrane (yet another result of the general surface repulsion force).

PROMETAPHASE

As in the case of mitosis we call the period between the disappearance of the nuclear membrane and the moment when the spindle is fully formed, prometaphase. At this stage the diakinesis bivalents have contracted still further and begin to be associated with the developing spindle. It will be remembered that at mitosis the contraction of the chromatids is due to the actual substance of which they are composed becoming 'spiralized'; that is to say each prometaphase or metaphase chromatid at mitosis consists of a cylindrical 'spring', possibly enclosed in some sort of sheath or pellicle. By special technical methods (exposure of the living material to ammonia vapour or fumes of strong acids before fixation) it has been shown [96], [98] that at meiosis

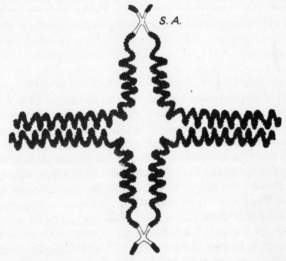

S. A.

FIG. 15.—Diagram of a bivalent at the first meiotic division showing the major and the minor spiral. The spindle attachments are subterminal and there is only one chiasma.

each chromatid probably forms a *double spiral* (Fig. 15), each gyre of the 'major' spiral being made up of several gyres of the 'minor' spiral. This may also be the case at mitosis, but so far only one spiral has been observed at ordinary somatic divisions.

METAPHASE OF FIRST MEIOTIC DIVISION

At mitosis each chromosome is attached to the spindle by a single spindle attachment (or one which has ,only just divided in prometaphase and whose component halves are still in contact). As a result all the spindle attachments lie in the equatorial plane. At meiosis, on the other hand, each bivalent possesses two spindle attachments, one belonging to the maternal chromosome, the other to the paternal one. These are in general fairly far apart and they arrange themselves at equal distances above and below the equatorial plane, i.e. between this and the poles of the spindle. *The spindle attachments have not divided, nor do they do so until the second meiotic division.*

ANAPHASE OF FIRST MEIOTIC DIVISION

At the anaphase of the first division the whole spindle attachments play the same rôle as the split halves of the spindle attachments play at an ordinary mitotic anaphase. As they separate (repelling one another exactly as the split halves do at mitosis) they drag after them the chromatids which are attached to them. As they do so the chiasmata which have not already been 'terminalized' move along to the ends of the bivalent away from the spindle attachment and slip off at the end. Chromosomes which are only associated by means of 'terminal chiasmata' are simply torn apart as the spindle attachments repel one another. Each spindle attachment as it moves towards the pole drags after it (either on the surface of the spindle or in its substance) two chromatids. If the spindle attachment is median or submedian these will form a structure with four arms of more or less equal length with the spindle attachment at their point of junction (as in the case of the larger chromosome in Fig. 10*h* and chromosome A in Fig. 16*a*). If, on the other hand, the spindle attachment is sub-terminal, two of the arms will be very short and the general appearance of the chromosome will be that of a V (smaller chromosome in Fig. 10*h* and chromosomes B and C in Fig. 16*a*).

The result of the first meiotic anaphase is often said to be a separation of whole chromosomes instead of the split halves of chromosomes as at mitosis. While this is correct in a sense it must be pointed out that the chromosomes which separate at the first anaphase are not the same as the maternal and paternal chromosomes which came together at zygotene ; these have interchanged sections of their

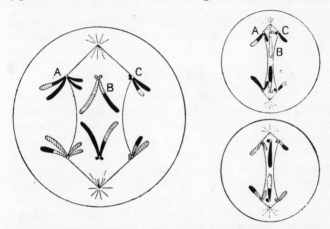

FIG. 16.—Diagrams showing the genetic consequences of the first and second meiotic divisions. Maternal portions black, paternal ones hatched. Three pairs of chromosomes are shown, each pair having possessed a single chiasma. It will be seen that the first division is always ' reductional ' between the spindle attachment and the first chiasma, and the second division is always ' equational ' for this region.

length by crossing over so that the actual chromosomes which separate at the first division are *new* combinations of segments of the maternal and paternal chromosomes (Fig. 16*a*). Between the spindle attachment and the first point of crossing-over on either side of it, however, the first anaphase always leads to the separation of two maternal from two paternal chromatids (Fig. 16).

5

Whether the maternal spindle attachment in a particular bivalent goes to the 'North' or the 'South' pole of the spindle (and vice versa) for the paternal one is a matter of chance ; it depends on which way up the bivalent has orientated itself at prometaphase. There is no correlation between the mode of orientation of one bivalent and another in the same cell. Thus in *Drosophila melanogaster* with four bivalents all paternal spindle attachments will go to the same pole once in 16 (2^4) times, in female Locusts and grasshoppers with 12 bivalents once in 4096 (2^{12}) ; while in man with 24 bivalents this event will only happen once in 16,777,216 (2^{24}) times. Exceptions to this rule occur under special circumstances in *Sciara*, *Oenothera* and *Drosophila miranda*.

As in the case of mitosis the first part of anaphase (during which the spindle attachments repel one another) is followed by a period during which the middle part of the spindle elongates so as to form a 'stem-body' and completes the anaphase separation of the two groups of chromosomes.

TELOPHASE

The telophase of the first meiotic division does not differ in any important respect from that of an ordinary somatic mitosis. The two telophase nuclei may pass into a more or less complete resting stage between the two meiotic divisions (*interphase* or *interkinesis*) in which the chromosomes become unfixable as in a somatic resting stage or they may remain condensed and undergo no changes between the anaphase of the first division and the metaphase of the second (Fig. 10*i*).

SECOND MEIOTIC DIVISION

If the chromosomes have not gone into a resting stage during interkinesis (a matter which is subject to a surprising amount of variation even in the same organism under different conditions) there will naturally be no prophase to the second division. In this case the telophase nuclei of the first division will pass directly (by loss of their nuclear membranes) into the prometaphase of the second division ; a spindle will develop and we have reached the metaphase of the second division by a ' short-cut ', involving the entire elimination of a prophase. In any case the prophase of the second division, even if present, is always short.

The prometaphase of the second division differs from that of an ordinary mitosis in two respects, (1) the number of chromosomes is half the somatic number, (2) the chromatids diverge widely, being only held together at the spindle attachment and not approximated throughout their length as at mitosis ; they tend, however, to come into closer contact at the metaphase of the second division. In some cases the second division chromosomes appear to resemble those of an ordinary mitosis in having only one spiral (and not a ' major ' and a ' minor ' one as at the first meiotic division).

ANAPHASE AND TELOPHASE OF THE SECOND DIVISION

These do not differ from those of an ordinary mitosis, so that it is not necessary to describe them in detail. Between the spindle attachment and the first point of crossing-over the second anaphase always leads to the separation of maternal from maternal chromatids or of paternal from paternal ones (Fig. 16).

One last question in connexion with meiosis remains to be considered. If the whole process has arisen by profound modification of two mitoses, and if the chromosome ' split ' of the first one is delayed until pachytene, what has happened to the ' split ' corresponding to the second division ? Usually there is no trace of it but various authors [97], [170] have claimed to have seen a split down the middle of the anaphase chromatids of the first division. Such a split, if

present, either closes up again, and is thus non-
functional, or else functions as the effective split at
the next division (in animals the first cleavage
division of the zygote, in Angiosperms the pollen
grain mitosis in microsporogenesis and the first
division of the embryo-sac nucleus in megasporo-
genesis).

CHAPTER V

SPECIAL PROBLEMS OF MEIOSIS

WE have seen in the preceding chapter that crossing-over is an event which normally happens at least once in every pair of chromosomes at meiosis. If a bivalent has a chiasma-frequency of 1·0 that means that on an average two out of the four chromatids undergo one cross-over, i.e. that between two points situated at opposite ends of the chromosome, crossing-over takes place in 50 per cent of cases. Thus a bivalent with a chiasma-frequency of 1·0 will have a length of 50 'genetic units'; similarly, bivalents with chiasma-frequencies of 2·0 and 3·48 will have map lengths of 100 and 174 units respectively. In mapping chromosomes genetically it is useful to know the total map-length in advance, and this can now be calculated from the cytologically determined chiasma-frequency in this simple way. Table VI shows the total calculated length of the genetic maps in maize and the length already known. It will be seen in no case does the known length exceed the total calculated length.

In many chromosomes it appears that chiasmata are as likely to be formed in one region as in another, so that if we divide the bivalent into n short lengths x microns long the chiasma-frequency of all of them will be the same. This appears to be the case in the long chromosomes of *Vicia faba*,[106] *Lilium* spp.,[116] *Stenobothrus* and *Chorthippus* [30, 39] and probably in a large number of other cases. In certain organisms, however, chiasmata are more or less restricted to definite regions. Thus in the female * *Drosophila melanogaster* an examination of the genetic map reveals the fact that the genes in Chromosomes II

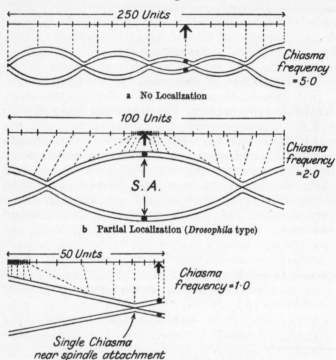

a   No Localization

b   Partial Localization (*Drosophila* type)

c   Complete Localization (*Mecostethus* type)

FIG. 17.—Diagrams of the relationship between chiasma-localization and genetic maps. Explanation in text.

and III are crowded in the central region round the spindle attachment; there is also a lesser degree of crowding at the ends, the genes between the ends and the central region being much more sparsely scattered (Fig. 17). By a study of chromosome breaks it has

* In *Drosophila* genetic maps only exist for the female sex, since no crossing-over normally takes place in the male (*vide infra*).

been possible to show that this is a 'genetical illusion '—in the actual physical chromosome the genes are approximately evenly spaced. The central region is shortened on the genetic map while the part between this and the ends is artificially magnified. This means that crossing-over takes place more often in this region than in a region of the same length near the spindle attachment ; there is a *partial localization* of chiasmata.

In a number of organisms—*Fritillaria* (Liliaceae), *Mecostethus* (Orthoptera, Acridiidae) and many Tettigoniidae—another type of localization is found in which chiasmata are entirely restricted to certain regions of the chromosomes (usually the region next to the spindle attachment). Thus in the grasshoppers of the genus *Mecostethus* there is usually a single chiasma in each bivalent which is situated very close to the spindle attachment.[181] In this, which is an extreme case, only those genes which lie

TABLE VI

CHIASMA-FREQUENCIES AND GENETIC LENGTH OF THE TEN CHROMOSOMES IN MAIZE (*ZEA MAYS*) [36]

| Chromosome | Chiasma-frequency | Map-length in genetic units | | Number of known genes |
		Total calculated	Already known	
1	3·65	183	102	7
2	3·25	163	58	6
3	3·00	150	92	7
4	2·95	148	80	10
5	2·95	148	44	6
6	2·20	110	52	5
7	2·45	123	50	7
8	2·45	123	20	2
9	2·20	110	52	7
10	1·95	98	68	3
Totals	27·05	1,353	618	60

near the spindle attachment could be 'mapped' genetically ; the others would show complete linkage and no crossing-over (Fig. 17). Unfortunately no genetical work has been done on these organisms with strict localization of chiasmata.

It is a fact which has long been known in genetics that the occurrence of a cross-over at a particular locus prevents crossing-over for a certain distance on either side. This phenomenon is known as *interference*. Cytologically it means that there must be a certain minimum distance between chiasmata. If, as previously suggested, crossing-over results from a torsional strain of some kind it is clear that this strain will be relieved in the adjoining region once crossing-over has taken place. That is to say, a chiasma diminishes the probability of another being formed in its immediate neighbourhood to zero and this ' interference ' falls off until at a certain distance from the first chiasma it is no longer present. In many small bivalents the total length of the chromosome is shorter than the region of complete interference so that only one chiasma is formed. HALDANE [61] has proved the existence of interference as a cytological phenomenon by a statistical analysis of chiasma-frequencies.

If one considers two adjacent chiasmata in a bivalent it is clear that the relationship between them may be of three different kinds : (1) the second chiasma may involve the *same two chromatids* as the first one, (2) it may involve one of those which crossed over in the first chiasma and one that did not, or (3) it may involve the two that did not cross over in the first chiasma. These three types of relationship are called *reciprocal, diagonal* and *complementary*.[158] If the second chiasma arose between the four chromatids at random then the three types would occur in the ratio 1 : 2 : 1. The reciprocal and complementary types of relationship cannot, unfortunately, be distinguished from one another cytologically; they are grouped together as *compensating* relationships. Direct observations on the relative frequencies of the compensating and non-compensating (diagonal) kinds of relationship have only been made in a few cases, but in the grasshopper *Melanoplus femur-rubrum* the compensating appear to be about twice as frequent as the non-compensating relationships.[64] Probably it is the complementary type which is unusually abundant; there would appear to be a kind of *chromatid interference* which usually prevents the same chromatids from participating in adjacent chiasmata.

MEIOSIS IN HYBRIDS

From the cytological point of view there are three main types of hybrids, ordinary diploid hybrids, *complex heterozygotes* (such as the Evening Primrose, *Oenothera* spp.) and polyploid hybrids (allo-polyploids). A diploid hybrid is an organism with its two haploid sets of chromosomes derived from different parent species. However similar they may be taxonomically these parent species will nearly always differ in respect of a number of genes; moreover, the extent of the taxonomic differences between two species is probably a very unreliable guide to the number of gene differences involved.

In addition to simple gene-differences the parents of a hybrid may also differ in the way in which the genes are arranged in the chromosomes. Thus in the case of *Drosophila melanogaster* and *D. simulans* (which are taxonomically so similar that they were originally regarded as one species), the number of chromosomes is the same and their relative lengths are almost identical, but a large portion of the IIIrd chromosome (about one-quarter of its total length) is inverted in *simulans* in comparison with *melanogaster*; in addition there are a number of differences in the sex-chromosomes and in Chromosome IV which are visible in the salivary gland nuclei and which are probably to be interpreted as multiple gene-differences.[145] Hybrids can be obtained between the two species, but they are sterile.

Inversions of the type just described are probably among the commonest cytological differences between closely related species (they occur also inside single species [37, 46]). In addition to these and single gene-differences, however, the parent species of a hybrid may differ in respect of (1) chromosome number, (2) chromosome size, and (3) rate and extent of contraction of the chromosomes at mitosis and meiosis. Where the chromosome numbers of the two parent species differ one of the two haploid sets in the hybrid will contain more chromosomes than the other and the ' extra ' chromosomes will necessarily be unable to pair at zygotene and will form univalents at the first meiotic division. As far as the others are concerned, there is a possibility of them all pairing and forming bivalents, but where the chromosome numbers of the two species differ the degree of homology between the two haploid sets is usually so incomplete that pairing and chiasma-formation only take place in a few chromosomes ; the number of univalents is thus usually considerably in excess of the number of ' extra ' chromosomes in such cases. For example, in hybrids between the moths *Saturnia pavonia* and *S. pyri* (haploid numbers 29 and 30 respectively) only about 5 to 6 bivalents are formed as a rule, the remaining 47 or 49 chromosomes being left as univalents.[144]

Where the chromosome numbers of the two parent species are the same *all* the chromosomes *may* pair but do not necessarily do so. Thus in the hybrids between the moths *Celerio euphorbiae* and *C. galii* (both with a haploid number of 29) each *euphorbiae* chromosome pairs with a *galii* one so that 29 bivalents and no univalents are formed. On the other hand, in the hybrid between *Pergesa elpenor* and *Celerio euphorbiae* (each with a haploid number of 29 as before) only about 4 bivalents are formed, the remaining 50 chromosomes being left as diploid univalents.[16] Finally, in diploid hybrids between the Cabbage and Radish no bivalents may occur, all the chromosomes forming univalents.[81, 82]

Univalent Chromosomes at Meiosis [153, 41, 83]

A univalent chromosome at meiosis may arise in two ways—it is either a chromosome which has never undergone pairing at zygotene, or else it is one which has paired to form a bivalent whose two component chromosomes have separated again at diplotene owing to the fact that no chiasma was formed between them. Most univalents are probably of the former type, but only a close study of all stages of meiosis can reveal the precise mode of origin in each particular case. The behaviour of univalents at the metaphase of the first meiotic division is interesting, although variable. Since they only possess one undivided spindle attachment (instead of two as in the case of a bivalent, or one which is in process of division as in a mitotic chromosome) they do not necessarily become associated with the spindle in the equatorial plane, but attach themselves anywhere between its two poles. As the bivalents separate into their component halves and pass to the poles the univalents are left in the central part of the spindle (the ' stem-body '). The first meiotic division may be completed without any separation of the univalents into their chromatids in which case they may (1) be distributed at random between the two nuclei, (2) form small supplementary nuclei enclosed in their own nuclear membranes, (3) mechanically prevent complete separation of the two main groups of chromosomes after the first division so that these come to be included in a single *diploid* interkinesis nucleus. Alternatively, (4) the spindle attachments of the univalents may finally undergo division at the end of the anaphase of the first division, so that the half-univalents pass to the poles although tardily. In the first three cases (where the spindle attachments of the univalents have not divided in the course of the first division) the univalents behave normally at the second division, separating into their component chromatid halves. In the fourth case the spindle attachments have divided and the univalents separated into their chromatid halves at the first division, and consequently do not divide at all at the second meiotic division, being passively distributed at random to the two poles.

MEIOSIS IN THE MALE DROSOPHILA AND IN OTHER DIPTERA

It is well known that in the males of *Drosophila* spp. no crossing-over normally takes place (under special conditions very rare cross-overs occur).[53] The reason for this has been cleared up by a recent investigation.[32] No chiasmata are normally formed in the autosomes ; if this were to take place in any other organism but a Dipteran it would lead to the bivalents separating into pairs of univalent chromosomes at diplotene, but owing to the strong ' somatic pairing ' (residual attraction) the two chromosomes of each bivalent do not fall apart, but remain associated until anaphase. In the case of the X and Y chromosomes it is usual for a pair of compensating chiasmata to be formed in the neighbourhood of the spindle attachment in a region which is inert and ' homologous '. The normal process of meiosis in the male *Drosophila* is thus highly modified, although in the female it follows the usual course.

In other Diptera such as species of the genus *Sciara* even more unusual types of meiosis are found in the males, although, as in *Drosophila*, oogenesis is entirely normal. Thus in the male diploid set of *Sciara coprophila* there are five pairs of chromosomes (one pair of large V's, one pair of medium-sized

V's and three pairs of rods). There is no pairing of chromosomes at zygotene and all ten behave as univalents. The spindle which forms at the prometa-phase of the first meiotic division is a half-spindle (see Fig. 3) to which *both* the large V-shaped chromosomes and one member of each of the other pairs are attached. The remaining chromosomes move away from the half-spindle ; there is genetic evidence that these four chromosomes which are unattached to the half-spindle are all paternal chromosomes. The first meiotic division thus separates a group of six chromosomes from a group of four—the latter degenerate in a small bud of cytoplasm which becomes cut off from the main cell like a polar body, while the group of six chromosomes proceed to the second meiotic division. Here a normal bipolar spindle is formed and five of the six chromosomes divide normally, but one of the rod-shaped chromosomes divides in such a way that both its halves go to the same pole. The group of chromosomes at this pole form a sperm nucleus, while the other group degener-ates. Only one sperm is thus formed from each primary spermatocyte and it contains more than the haploid number of chromosomes.[125] A complicated mechanism involving the elimination of certain chromosomes occurs during the cleavage divisions.[47] It is clear that this type of meiosis is even more highly modified from the normal type than that found in *Drosophila*, and that it involves a complete suppression of crossing-over in the male. In the female *Sciara*, on the other hand, meiosis is entirely normal. A similar type of meiosis appears to occur in the male Hessian Fly (*Phytophaga destructor*).[120]

GENETICALLY DETERMINED ABNORMALITIES OF MEIOSIS

A fairly large number of gene-mutations are now known which lead to abnormalities of meiosis. Most of these mutations interfere with chiasma-formation, and consequently lead to very irregular distribution of the chromosomes at the first meiotic division. Such genes are known in Maize, *Nicotiana* and other plants. In *Drosophila melanogaster* ' Gowen's Gene ' produces similar effects on meiosis in the female.[55]

BEHAVIOUR OF SEX-CHROMOSOMES AT MEIOSIS

We have briefly considered (Chap. III) the different types of sex-chromosomes as they appear at mitosis; it remains to be seen what happens to them at meiosis. In the homogametic sex they behave, in general, just like autosomes. Their behaviour in the heterogametic sex depends on the following general principles :

(1) Non-homologous regions of chromosomes do not pair, and consequently no chiasmata can be formed between them.

(2) Homologous regions do pair at zygotene, even though other regions of the chromosomes in question are not homologous. Chiasmata will be formed in the homologous paired regions, unless these are very short.

(3) Pairing may be prevented, even between homologous regions, by extreme positive heteropycnosis.

(4) Univalent sex-chromosomes (i.e. sex-chromosomes with no chiasmata) behave like other univalent chromosomes and may show either the first or the fourth type of behaviour described above.

Having stated these general principles we can consider specific cases. In Locusts and Grasshoppers we encounter one of the most highly evolved types of sex-determining mechanism, which is, however, one of the simplest to understand. The male is the heterogametic sex, and there is no Y-chromosome ; (that is to say, the female diploid set includes two X-chromosomes, the male set only one, which is consequently a univalent at meiosis). The X in the male shows intense positive heteropycnosis in its distal half (i.e. that farthest away from the spindle attachment which is almost terminal) throughout zygotene and pachytene. This heteropycnosis extends to the proximal half during diakinesis and prometaphase, after which de-condensation usually begins to set in. The X-chromosome associates itself with the spindle of the first meiotic division somewhere between the equator and one of the poles. Its spindle attachment does not divide at the first division and consequently both the chromatid halves of the X go to the same pole. Thus two kinds of secondary spermatocytes are formed, one with, the other without an X-chromosome. At the second division the X divides and goes to both poles in those secondary spermatocytes in which it is present. Thus in this case the univalent X shows the first type of behaviour of the four mentioned above. The opposite condition where a single X divides in the first meiotic division and goes undivided to one pole in the second division is met with in some other insects (the Beetle *Photinus* and the Bugs *Anasa tristis*, *Alydus* and *Protenor*).[169, 186, 150, 163] The Locust *Schistocerca* and the Bug *Archimerus* also illustrate the truth of the third principle (that extreme positive heteropycnosis may prevent either pairing or chiasma-formation or both) since even in polyploid spermatocytes containing two or three X-chromosomes these behave as univalents, although they lie very close to one another, as a result of an attraction analogous to 'somatic pairing'[178, 188] (Fig. 18).

A more complicated type of sex-determining mechanism is found in mammals, where both an X and a Y are present in the male. In the Rat[94] the two sex-chromosomes both have submedian spindle attachments. There is a region in the Y which is homologous to a corresponding region in the X. This region includes the spindle attachments in both chromosomes and extends as far as one end of the chromosome. The remaining parts of the two chromosomes are not homologous. Thus each sex-chromosome consists of two segments, a *pairing segment* and a *differential segment* (Fig. 8). The two pairing segments come together at zygotene and chiasmata are later formed between them on either side of the spindle attachments or on both sides. An *XY bivalent* is thus formed. At the first meiotic division the differential segments of the X and Y go to opposite poles and at the second division they divide in the ordinary way. The sex-determining mechanism in man is probably of this type but the details have not yet been worked out. In some Marsupials the sex-chromosomes are essentially of the same kind as in the Rat, but the spindle attachments appear to lie in the differential region.[93]

In *Drosophila melanogaster* we again have an XY bivalent formed in the male ; the pairing segment includes the spindle attachment and is genetically inert. The X-chromosome has a single differential segment which includes the spindle attachment and contains all the ' sex-linked ' genes except *bobbed*, while the Y has two differential segments, one on either side of the pairing segment.

In some Bugs (*Rhynchota*) no pairing of the X- and Y-chromosomes takes place at the first division. This may be due to there being no common homologous pairing region, or it may mean that pairing is prevented at zygotene by positive heteropycnosis. In *Lygaeus*, at any rate,[185] the latter explanation seems to be the more probable one. Both the X and the Y divide at the first meiotic division so that the two secondary spermatocytes which are formed have the same chromosome set. At the second meiotic division the X- and Y-chromosomes come into extremely close approximation ; it is probable that this is a delayed zygotene pairing of short homologous regions which is rendered possible by

decondensation of the heteropycnotic sex-chromosomes between the two divisions. It results in the
chromosomes orientating themselves in the long
axis of the second division spindle, above and below
the equatorial plane, so that one goes to each pole
(cf. *Anasa*, *Alydus* and *Protenor*, where there is a
similar mechanism but without a Y).

In organisms with an X^1X^2Y mechanism (e.g.
the Praying Mantis) each X has a pairing region
homologous to a corresponding pairing region in the
Y. No region in X^1 is homologous to any part of
X^2, so that X^1 and X^2 never pair together but
always with different parts of the Y.[88] The converse
situation occurs in *Rumex acetosa* where Y^1 and Y^2
pair separately with parts of the X.[159] Thus in
both cases a *sex-trivalent* is formed with its three
component chromosomes held together by chiasmata.
In *Mantis* X^1 and X^2 go to the same pole at the
first division, Y going to the other pole, in *Rumex
acetosa* Y^1 and Y^2 go to one pole and X to the other.

MEIOSIS IN HAPLOID ORGANISMS

In Insects with male haploidy it is usual for the
first meiotic division to be entirely suppressed so
that the sperms are formed with the same number
of chromosomes as the somatic tissues of the adult
male. Vestiges of the first meiotic division do occur,
however, in most cases. Thus in the male Bee
(drone) the prophase stages of the first meiotic
division take place, but the metaphase and anaphase
are entirely omitted ; the second meiotic division
then follows [134] ; in some other haploid insects the
first division is even more completely suppressed.[69]
In plants, on the other hand, where haploid sporo-
phytes occur occasionally, both meiotic divisions
usually occur. In ' true ' haploids all the chromosomes behave as univalents, dividing in either the
first or the second division, but never in both.
Some haploid plants, however, have small sections

6

of the chromosomes reduplicated in other members of the chromosome set ; in these cases the small reduplicated sections may pair at zygotene and form chiasmata later, so that there are a few bivalents at the first meiotic division.[21] Plants like this are clearly not true haploids ; they are really intermediate between the diploid and the true haploid condition.

MEIOSIS IN POLYPLOID ORGANISMS

Where there are more than two homologous chromosomes of each kind in the somatic set three or more may become paired at zygotene—but never more than two at any one point. Thus in a triploid if we consider three homologous chromosomes A_1, A_2 and A_3, A_1 may pair with A_2 in one region and with A_3 in another, but A_1, A_2 and A_3 are never associated together in the same region.[138] On the other hand, A_1 may pair with A_2 throughout its entire length (to form a bivalent) in which case A_3 will be left unpaired and form a univalent. Thus in a triploid organism *trivalents*, bivalents, and univalents may be found in the same nucleus. Similarly, in a tetraploid *quadrivalents* may be found in addition to the three other types and in higher polyploids *quinquevalents* and *hexavalents* may also occur. All associations of more than two chromosomes can be spoken of collectively as *multivalents*. The frequency of formation of multivalents in polyploids varies a great deal and apparently depends in part on the length of the chromosomes and in part on the rapidity of zygotene pairing.[178] Where the chromosomes are long and pairing is slow the probability of multivalent formation is high, where the chromosomes are short and pairing is rapid it will be low. Other factors such as the ratio of the volume of the chromosomes to the volume of the nucleus and the arrangement of the chromosomes at zygotene (random or polarized—see Chap. IV) also affect the fre-

quency of multivalent formation.   Another factor of
major importance in this connexion is whether the
polyploid in question is an auto- or an allo-polyploid ;
allo-polyploids form far fewer multivalents than auto-
polyploids.   Thus if we consider an allo-tetraploid
with four chromosomes A_1, A_2, A_3' and A_4' (A_1 and
A_2 being derived from one parent species and A_3'
and A_4' from the other) it will probably form two

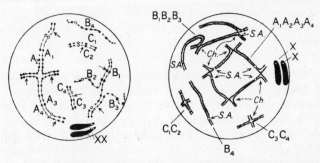

a   Two-Strand Pachytene   b   Diplotene

FIG. 18.—Diagrams of meiosis in a male tetraploid organism
    which has a somatic chromosome set of twelve autosomes
    and two X-chromosomes.   One quadrivalent ($A_1A_2A_3A_4$)
    one trivalent ($B_1B_2B_3$), two bivalents (C_1C_2 and C_3C_4),
    and a univalent (B_4) are formed among the autosomes.
    The two X-chromosomes are held together in close
    association as a result of a pairing-attraction, but do not
    form any chiasmata on account of their strong positive
    heteropycnosis.   In a the positions where the chiasmata
    will subsequently arise are indicated by arrows.   S.A. =
    spindle attachment, ch = chiasmata.

bivalents (A_1, A_2) and (A_3', A_4') since although all
the chromosomes are partly homologous those derived
from the same parent are completely so.   An idea
of the range of variation as regards multivalent
formation can be got from Table VII which shows
the frequency with which quadrivalents are formed
in auto-tetraploids.

The general history of multivalents at meiosis
(chiasma-formation,   shifting   of   chiasmata,   &c.)

TABLE VII

FREQUENCY OF QUADRIVALENT-FORMATION IN AUTO-
TETRAPLOIDS

Organism	Maximum possible no. of Quadrivalents	Actual no. (average)
Artemia salina	21	0·0
Tulipa stellata	12	0·5
Schistocerca gregaria . .	11	3·0
Primula sinensis . . .	12	10·4
Datura Stramonium . .	12	12·0

follows the usual course already described in the case
of bivalents. When they come to orientate themselves on the spindle of the first division they do so
in a way which can be explained if there is, in
addition to the general repulsion force between all
chromosome surfaces, an extra repulsion force
between spindle attachments. Thus in the case of
a trivalent it is usual for two spindle attachments to
go to one pole and the one between them to the
other. In the case of quadrivalents two spindle
attachments go to each pole. Which of the four
go to the same pole depends in part on whether they
lie in the middle of the chromosomes or almost at
one end and in part on the number of chiasmata
which have been formed in the quadrivalent. In
nuclei with only quadrivalents and bivalents an
equal number of chromosomes will go to the two
poles at the first division, but in those with univalents, trivalents or quinquevalents the number of
chromosomes going to the poles will generally be
unequal.

MEIOSIS IN COMPLEX HETEROZYGOTE
ORGANISMS [29, 35, 21]

In many species of the genus *Oenothera* (Evening
Primroses) and in some other plants such as *Hyperi-*

cum punctatum [67] and *Rhoeo discolor* [91] it is not possible to arrange the somatic chromosomes in pairs ;
that is to say that no one chromosome is completely
homologous to any other. Only as a result of long
genetical and cytological work has it been possible to
understand exactly what happens during the meiosis
of such organisms. The following account is necessarily somewhat simplified but is substantially true.

If the chromosomes of an ordinary diploid organism
with a haploid number of 4 be represented as follows :

$$abcdef \qquad ghij$$
$$abcdef \qquad ghij$$

$$klmno \qquad pqrst$$
$$klmno \qquad pqrst$$

then those of *Oenothera muricata* will be :

$$abC_1cd \qquad lkR_3mn \qquad vuC_6wx$$
$$dcR_1ef \qquad nmC_4op \qquad xwR_6yz$$
$$feC_2gh \qquad poR_4qr \qquad zyC_7\alpha\beta$$
$$hgR_2ij \qquad rqC_5st \qquad \beta\alpha R_7ba$$
$$jiC_3kl \qquad tsR_5uv$$

It will be seen that each chromosome consists of
three segments, two *terminal ones* (represented by
the small letters) and a *median one* (represented by
the capital C's and R's). The median segment contains the spindle attachment in all cases. None of
the median segments are homologous (i.e. they are
differential segments analogous to those present in
sex-chromosomes) ; the terminal segments in each
chromosome are, however, homologous to two other
terminal segments *in different* chromosomes. Thus
when pairing takes place at zygotene it does not
generally affect the median segments * but only the
terminal ones (Fig. 19a). At pachytene a con-

* The median segments are sometimes partially homologous, in which case they may pair and form occasional
chiasmata (see Chap. VI).

tinuous ring of chromosomes is formed instead of a number of bivalents. Chiasmata arise in the paired terminal segments so that the ring is maintained up to the metaphase of the first meiotic division. Occasionally a chiasma fails to develop in one of the paired terminal regions, so that the ring breaks at one point to give an open chain. It is obvious from the homologies of the pairing regions that the relative positions of the 14 chromosomes in the ring are constant.

At the prometaphase of the first division the spindle attachments arrange themselves in a zig-zag round the equator of the spindle so that alternate ones go to the same pole at anaphase (Fig. 19d). This is a natural consequence of the repulsion between the spindle attachments, and is a phenomenon we have already met in the case of trivalents. It results in all the C median segments going to one pole and the R ones to the other. C_1 . . . C_7 and R_1 . . . R_7 are thus inherited as units and are referred to in the genetical terminology as the *curvans* and *rigens complexes Oenothera muricata* thus consists of a rigens complex, a curvans complex and seven pairing segments each of which is represented twice in the somatic chromosome set.

The process of meiosis is essentially the same in macro- and micro-sporogenesis so that two kinds of megaspores and two kinds of pollen grains are formed. One of these contains the curvans segments C_1-C_7 and the other the rigens segments R_1-R_7. Fertilization of a curvans ovule by a curvans pollen tube or a rigens ovule by a rigens pollen tube leads, however, to an inviable type of zygote. Thus only the curvans × rigens and rigens × curvans zygotes survive and the species is kept in a state of permanent heterozygosity as far as the middle parts of its chromosomes are concerned.

The condition described above, in which all the chromosomes form a ring is found in a number of species of Oenothera, but not in all. In the remainder intermediate stages between this condition

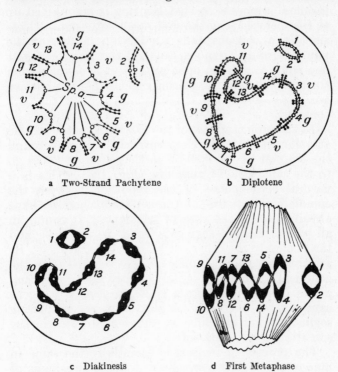

a Two-Strand Pachytene   b Diplotene

c Diakinesis   d First Metaphase

FIG. 19.—Diagrams of the First Meiotic Division in *Oenothera lamarckiana*. The chromosomes are labelled 1–14. 1 and 2 form a bivalent, being homologous throughout. 3–14 form a ring of 12 chromosomes united by 12 chiasmata after diplotene. The middle segments containing the *velans* and *gaudens* genes are labelled *v* and *g*. These segments contain the median spindle attachments. At anaphase chromosomes 3, 5, 7, 9, 11 and 13 go to one pole, 4, 6, 8, 10, 12 and 14 to the other.

and normal homozygosity are found. Thus in *Oenothera lamarckiana* a ring of twelve chromosomes and a single bivalent are formed at meiosis, in *Oe.*

biennis two rings (of eight and six chromosomes respectively) and in *Oe. franciscana* a ring of four and five bivalents; *Oe. Hookeri* is completely homozygous and forms seven bivalents. We can represent the chromosomes of the first two species as follows (the ' complexes ' are called *velans* and *gaudens* in *Oe. lamarckiana*, *rubens* and *albicans* in *Oe. biennis*) :

<table>
<tr><td colspan="2" align="center">*Oe. lamarckiana*</td><td colspan="2" align="center">*Oe. biennis*</td></tr>
<tr><td>$abcd$</td><td>poG_3qr</td><td>baR_1cd</td><td>poA_4qr</td></tr>
<tr><td>$abcd$</td><td>rqV_4st</td><td>dcA_1ef</td><td>rqR_1st</td></tr>
<tr><td>feV_1gh</td><td>tsG_4uv</td><td>efR_2gh</td><td>tsA_1uv</td></tr>
<tr><td>hgG_1j_4</td><td>vuV_5wx</td><td>hgA_2ij</td><td>vuR_6wx</td></tr>
<tr><td>jiV_2kl</td><td>xwG_5yz</td><td>jiR_3kl</td><td>xwA_6yz</td></tr>
<tr><td>lkG_2mn</td><td>$zyV_6\alpha\beta$</td><td>lkA_3ab</td><td>$zyR_7\alpha\beta$</td></tr>
<tr><td>nmV_3op</td><td>$\beta\alpha G_6ef$</td><td>nmR_4op</td><td>$\beta\alpha A_7mn$</td></tr>
</table>

Rings of four, six or more chromosomes are formed at the first meiotic division in a number of other plant genera (*Campanula*, *Pisum*, &c.) and from a study of these cases (some of which, notably *Pisum*, have arisen under experimental conditions) it has been possible to explain the origin of the whole mechanism (Chap. VI).

CHAPTER VI

CHROMOSOMES AND EVOLUTION

TWO different concepts are included in the term
evolution and are frequently confused with
one another—morphological change and the formation of new species. There has recently been a
tendency to regard the species as a category which
varies from group to group, so that a ' species '
of beetle is not equivalent to a ' species ' of primate
or conifer. From a morphological point of view this
is no doubt true—the extent of the taxonomic
differences between species do vary from group to
group. But from a genetical point of view the
species (i.e. a group of individuals all of which normally and regularly breed together except in so far
as they may be separated by geographical isolation)
is still a satisfactory concept which only breaks down
in organisms which reproduce without fertilization.

With the exception of a small number of cytoplasmic characters in plants (and possibly also in animals,
but there is no well-established case as yet) all evolutionary changes have clearly arisen in the first place
as changes in the chromosomes. It was formerly
believed that these changes were of two main types :
gene-mutations (which were conceived of as sub-
microscopic molecular changes) and *structural alterations* in chromosomes (i.e. microscopically visible
rearrangement of whole blocks of genes by translocation, inversion, &c.). It has recently been shown,
however,[132] that this distinction is rather one of
degree than of kind ; most (possibly *all*) gene-mutations are minute structural alterations involving

the rearrangement of a small section of a chromosome.

The detailed analysis of evolution by cytological and genetical methods has only just begun. Already, however, one thing is clear—the mechanism of evolution (or at any rate the mechanism of species-formation) has not been the same in all groups of organisms. Translocation and inversion of chromosome segments, hybridization, auto- and allo-polyploidy are the raw materials of species formation ; but they have contributed to different degrees in different groups of organisms. The mechanism of evolution has varied from group to group and even from genus to genus, so that it is becoming increasingly difficult to formulate general ' laws ' of evolution, and the universal applicability of such ' laws ' as have been derived from palaeontology and morphology is becoming more and more doubtful.

The chief limiting factor in determining the mechanism of evolution in a group of organisms is the method of reproduction and the mode of sex-determination. At least five main types of life-cycle can be distinguished, each of which probably possesses a highly variable system of evolution and species formation :

1. Clonal or vegetative reproduction (Meiosis and Fertilization absent or non-functional).
2. Sexual reproduction in Hermaphrodite organisms with self- or cross-fertilization.
3. Sexual reproduction in Complex Heterozygote organisms.
4. Sexual reproduction in dioecious organisms with a chromosomal sex-determining mechanism.
5. Sexual reproduction in organisms with male haploidy.

SPECIES-FORMATION IN ANGIOSPERMS

If one makes a list of the known haploid chromosome-numbers in the species of higher plants and animals one finds that in the case of the Angiosperms there is an excess of even over odd haploid numbers amounting to over 40 per cent, while in the case of animals the numbers of even and odd haploid numbers are not significantly unequal (Tables VIII and IX). This figure of 40 per cent gives a lower limit to the number of polyploid species of Angiosperms. *At least* 40 per cent of all Angiosperm species are tetraploid, hexaploid, &c. There is no other reason why more even than odd haploid numbers should exist and a detailed investigation of the frequency of particular numbers [209] bears out the general conclusion. One cannot set an upper limit to the extent to which polyploidy has occurred in plants, since aneuploids and other ' derived polyploids ' are not included in the above minimum figure. Neither is it possible to estimate the extent to which *all* Angiosperms have a more or less remote polyploid ancestry. It is also difficult to judge the relative importance of auto- and allo-polyploidy. The distinction between them is, however, only a relative one, since, on the one hand, allo-polyploids exist which are the result of hybridization between very closely related parent species or varieties and, on the other hand, independent mutation in the two diploid sets of an auto-tetraploid will give rise to an organism which will, like an allo-tetraploid, have a number of genetic differences between its two diploid chromosome sets. Thus in two ways forms will arise which are essentially intermediate between auto- and allo-polyploids in their genetic constitution.

Whatever their origin, all even-numbered polyploids (tetraploids, hexaploids, &c.) will, as a result of independent mutation in their multiple chromosome sets, tend to evolve towards a new condition of genetical diploidy, in which no gene will be represented more than twice in the chromosome set. There can be no doubt that many plant species represent stages in this process. Mutations are less likely to prove lethal in a tetraploid than in a diploid, since two of the four genes (and similarly four of the six in a hexaploid) are more or less superfluous and can consequently mutate without vitally affecting some important process as usually happens when the genes of a diploid mutate.

It seems fairly clear that a number of new Angiosperm genera have arisen as a result of hybridization between fairly widely separated species followed by allo-polyploidy, just as *Raphanobrassica* (allo-tetraploid Raddish-Cabbage hybrid) and *Aegilotriticum* (allo-polyploid Wheat-Rye hybrid) have arisen under experiment.   It is at any rate certain that well-marked species like *Aesculus carnea*, *Galeopsis Tetrahit*, *Spartina Townshendii*, and the American form of *Phleum pratense*, have arisen in the first place as allo-polyploids.[66, 133, 72, 58]   On the other hand where several chromosome numbers which are multiples of the lowest one exist within the same species of plant (as in *Biscutella laevigata* (see Chap. III) and *Nasturtium officinale*,[113] they are clearly due to auto-polyploidy.   Such auto-polyploid varieties are usually taxonomically distinguishable from the diploid form and from one another by slight morphological differences and may form the starting-point for new species if, as is usually the case, their hybrids with the diploid form or with one another are more or less sterile.   It is probably in this way that the species of the genus *Rumex* (section *Lapathum*) have originated (Table V).

Although polyploidy has undoubtedly taken place in nearly all the larger plant genera, and been responsible for the origin of a large number of species, there are some genera such as *Carex* where the known somatic chromosome numbers (18, 30, 32, 38, 52, 54, 56, 62, 64, 68, 70, 72, 74, 76, 80, 82) do not suggest that it has played any important part in the formation of new species.   The reason for this is not clear ; perhaps the actual formation of polyploid cells is rare in a genus like Carex, or perhaps polyploid individuals are considerably less viable than diploid ones.

ORIGIN OF COMPLEX HETEROZYGOTE ORGANISMS

Hypericum punctatum [67] is the only species of its genus which is a complex heterozygote, all the other St. John's Worts being normal diploids ; its evolutionary origin is thus extraordinarily interesting, but cannot be analysed. *Rhoeo discolor* is the only representative of its genus, so that here again we have no method of determining the origin of the complex-heterozygote mechanism. The genus Oenothera, on the other hand, contains a series of forms ranging from ordinary diploid species to organisms which form a ring of fourteen chromosomes at meiosis (see Chap. V).

If we take one of the diploid species of Oenothera which must be regarded as ancestral to those which form rings we can consider two pairs of chromosomes :

$$abcdefghi \qquad \text{and} \qquad mnopqrst$$
$$abcdefghi \qquad\qquad\qquad mnopqrst$$

If a reciprocal exchange (mutual translocation) takes place between one member of each pair of chromosomes it will give rise to two new chromosomes : *abcpqrst* and *mnodefghi*. The four chromosomes :

$$abcdefghi \qquad mnopqrst$$
$$abcpqrst \qquad mnodefghi$$

will now form a ring at meiosis ; but there will not be any ' median segment ' in such a ring ; on the other hand, if a second reciprocal interchange takes place it will establish a median segment if it does not correspond in position with the first. The second interchange may result from normal crossing-over if the first one was interstitial instead of terminal. By a repetition of this process rings of 6, 8, 10 and higher numbers can arise. The ring-forming species of

Oenothera produce trisomic gametes fairly often as a result of one chromosome in the ring going to the wrong pole at the first meiotic division. They also produce new types of gametes as a result of occasional chiasma-formation in the median segments. The 'mutants' of De Vries (on which he based his 'Mutationstheorie') were not really due to genetical mutation, but to occasional cross-overs of this type.

ORIGIN OF NEW SPECIES IN BISEXUAL ORGANISMS

In animals (with the exception of a few parthenogenetic and hermaphrodite groups such as the Pulmonata, Oligochaeta and in some Lepidoptera and Crustacea) polyploidy is entirely absent and consequently cannot account for the origin of new species. On the other hand the variation in chromosome number is almost as great in animals as in plants (cf. Tables VIII and IX). It is therefore clear that various mechanisms exist whereby chromosome numbers can be altered, and it is probable that these are closely connected with the origin of new species in some cases. It used to be supposed [187] that two or more chromosomes could merely fuse together to form a single one, and alternatively that one chromosome could break into a number of pieces, each of which would behave in future as a separate chromosome. If this were so a study of chromosome numbers would be of little importance. We now know, however, that each chromosome contains a single spindle attachment which is a self-perpetuating body ; new spindle attachments only arise from pre-existing ones.[136] Moreover, although spindle attachments divide longitudinally at mitosis, they do not appear to be transversely divisible. It is possible that in some cases V-shaped chromosomes have two spindle attachments in the middle only separated by a very short interstitial region ; in this case the two spindle attachments may be expected to function mechanically as a single unit, as in the case of *Ascaris megalocephala*. Breakage of the interstitial region will give two chromosomes with quasi-terminal spindle attachments (' rod-shaped ' chromosomes). Conversely two chromosomes with quasi-terminal spindle attachments may fuse together so as to give a V with two attachments in the middle. Any other kind of fusion will give a chromosome with two widely separated spindle attachments which will break at anaphase (Fig. 6) and any other kind of breakage will give rise to a fragment with no spindle attachment, which consequently cannot form an independent chromosome. Thus apart from these two special cases it does not seem possible that ' fusion and fragmentation ' have played any part in the evolution of new chromosome numbers.

In some groups of animals the chromosome number is fairly constant, while in others it varies from species to species. Thus nearly all Urodeles have a diploid number of 24, while in the Crickets (*Gryllodea*) thirteen different chromosome numbers have been found, ranging from 12 to 30 (in the female diploid set).[142] In some cases, where it is due to the processes described above, the origin of new chromosome numbers is clear. Thus most species of *Acrididae* (Locusts and Grasshoppers) have 11 pairs of rod-shaped autosomes with quasi-terminal spindle attachments, but in the genera *Chorthippus*, *Stenobothrus* and *Stauroderus* there are only 8 pairs, 3 of which are V-shaped, with median or submedian spindle attachments. The South American species *Aleuas vitticollis* has 9 pairs, two of which are V's.[155] It is clear that here originally separate chromosomes with subterminal spindle attachments have fused together so as to decrease the number of autosomes. Whether the V-shaped autosomes in these genera have two spindle attachments situated very close together is not certain, but appears probable; the only alternative would be to suppose that one spindle attachment had been lost in each case as a result of a deletion'. In the first case the formation of V's would be a reversible phenomenon, in the second it obviously would not. The only other aberrant chromosome number in the Acrididae is found in the species *Podisma mikado* which has only 10 pairs of rod-shaped autosomes.[111] In view of the remarkable constancy of the chromosome set in the whole family this is very surprising, particularly as the related species *P. sapporoense* appears to have the usual number of 11 pairs of autosomes. Whether a whole pair of autosomes (possibly genetically inert?) has been lost in *P. mikado*, or whether all of it except the spindle attachment has been translocated to another pair of autosomes and the spindle attachments lost cannot be decided at present.

If one examines a number of groups of animals one finds that there is a correlation between variation in size and variation in number of chromosomes which is sufficiently striking to be significant. Thus in groups such as the genus *Drosophila* and in the *Lacertilia* there are nearly always a number of very small chromosomes in the set which may be only just above the limit of resolution of the microscope (like the IVth chromosome in *D. melanogaster*, the Vth in *D. pseudo-obscura*, the VIth in *D. virilis* and the *microchromosomes* of Lacertilia and Birds). Usually, but not always, there is a sharp difference in size between the microchromosomes and the ordinary ones, with no intermediates (as in the genus *Drosophila*). A particularly interesting case is that of the *Urodela*; the majority of these (all species of *Triton*, *Salamandra*, *Amphiuma*, &c.) have 24 large chromosomes with median or submedian spindle attachments (Fig. 4). Where, as in the genera *Cryptobranchus*, *Megalobatrachus* and *Hynobius*, [109, 110, 74] there are more than 24 the extra ones are small microchromosomes. In view of what has been said above about spindle attachments, it is clear that the microchromosomes must have arisen as duplications of the spindle attachment regions of the larger chromosomes. We have already seen that in some and perhaps in all species of *Drosophila* the regions round the spindle attachments are genetically inert ; it seems at least possible that in other groups with microchromosomes the same is the case ; if this were so no upset of the ' genic balance ' would result when a spindle attachment region was reduplicated in the chromosome set. Perhaps in groups like the Acrididae, with a remarkable constancy of chromosome number, the regions round the spindle attachments are genetically active. The importance of microchromosomes lies in the fact that, once they have arisen, one or more translocations from other chromosomes may convert a microchromosome into one of normal size.

Duplication of a whole chromosome (polysomy) or even duplication of a relatively large region probably always upsets the ' genic balance ' and leads to the production of an organism which is less viable than the original one. It is obvious that the condition of maximum unbalance is reached when half the total chromosome set has been reduplicated (i.e. when the somatic chromosome number is mid-way between diploidy and triploidy).[36] It seems clear that in actual fact only very small duplications are likely to become established as new additions to the chromosome set. That they really do so is proved conclusively by the work of BRIDGES on the salivary gland chromosomes.[14] He found that a number of small regions which could be recognized by the characteristic sequence of bands were repeated or duplicated. There are several possible ways in which this may occur ; if we consider a region involving four bands, $p \, q \, r \, s$, these may be repeated in the same chromosome in any of the following four ways :

(1) *abcdefghijklmnopqrspqrstuvwxyz*

(2) *abcdefghijklmnopqrssrqptuvwxyz*

(3) *abcdefpqrsghijklmnopqrstuvwxyz*

(4) *abcdefsrqpghijklmnopqrstuvwxyz*

The ' reversed duplications ' (types 2 and 4) appear to be commoner than the ' direct ' ones (types 1 and 3), but the data are not as yet sufficient to form an opinion as to whether there is any special significance in this. In addition to duplications within the same chromosome, duplications of small regions probably also occur in other non-homologous chromosomes of the same set.

Duplication of the spindle attachment region is obviously a phenomenon of an entirely different nature to duplication of other regions ; if it takes place without the region in question being attached (either terminally or interstitially) to a pre-existing chromosome it will lead directly to the production of a new microchromosome as an addition to the chromosome set. It is this process which may have led to the appearance of microchromosomes in many groups of animals. On the other hand, if it happens in such a way that the duplication is at first attached to one of the original chromosomes (or inserted into it in an interstitial position) a chromosome with two spindle attachments will have arisen. Such a chromosome will break at about half the mitoses in each cell-generation. There is no reason why it should break at the junction between the duplicated and the non-duplicated region and consequently this process, while increasing the number of the chromosomes by one, will not necessarily give rise to a microchromosome, but may equally well give rise to a chromosome of a relatively large size.

BRIDGES' discovery (if it applies to animals in general, and not only to *Drosophila melanogaster*) means that so-called diploid species are really only partially diploid, a certain number of chromosome

regions being present in the tetraploid condition.   It
should eventually be possible to ascertain the *diploid-
tetraploid ratio* in different species of *Drosophila*.
The evolutionary significance of duplications is, as
Bridges points out, that they offer ' a method of
evolutionary increase in length of chromosomes with
identical genes which could subsequently mutate
separately and diversify their effects '.   It has already
been pointed out that mutations which may be lethal
when homozygous in a diploid are often quite viable
when present twice in a tetraploid.   Thus mutations
will be more likely to establish themselves in the
duplicated part of the chromosomes than in the
remainder.   The diploid-tetraploid ratio may thus
be one of the factors determining the rate of evolution
in a species or group.   Perhaps the shark *Scaphano-
rhynchus owstoni* which has existed unchanged from
the Upper Cretaceous to the present day has almost
no tetraploid regions in its chromosome set, and
perhaps duplications may be only very rarely produced in some groups (or be almost always lethal,
which comes to the same thing).

Formation of Species in the Genus Drosophila

The genus *Drosophila* has now been investigated
sufficiently for it to be possible to make some definite
statements as to how new species have arisen (the
problem of *species-dichotomy* as distinct from the
problem of *species-differentiation*).

In the first place the chromosome number varies
considerably from species to species (Table X).   Those
species with a high proportion of rod-shaped chromosomes have the highest numbers, those (like *D.
ananassae*) with all the chromosomes V-shaped have
the lowest numbers.   But it is clear from the Table
that not all the changes in chromosome number can
be accounted for by fusion of rods to form V's and
vice versa ; even if we assume that all V's have two
spindle attachments there is still a variation in

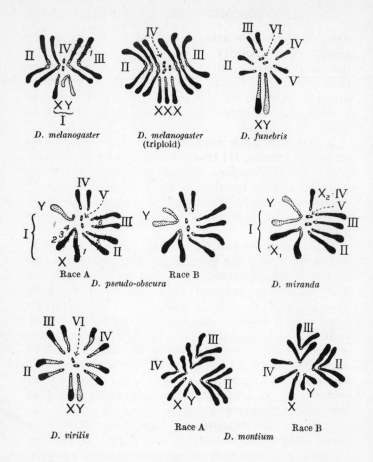

Fig. 20.—Somatic chromosome sets of various species of *Drosophila*; all male except the triploid *D. melanogaster*. Genetically active parts of chromosomes black, inert parts stippled. Inversion between *D. melanogaster* and *D. simulans* and between the A and B races of *D. pseudo-obscura* labelled 1, 2, 3, 4. . . . In *D. montium* the extent of the inert regions is not known so that they have not been indicated. The microchromosomes have been drawn as if they had median spindle attachments, but nothing is really known as to the exact location of the spindle attachments.

number of spindle attachments of 10 to 16 in the
genus. The majority of species have one pair of
microchromosomes, but not all ; no species has more
than one pair of them. There is so far no means of
ascertaining whether the pair of microchromosomes
is always homologous throughout those species in
which it is found.

It is worth while concentrating attention on two
groups of species, (1) that which includes *D. melanogaster* and *D. simulans*, (2) the *obscura* group, which
includes a large number of forms of which only *D.
sub-obscura*, *D. miranda* and the various races of
D. pseudo-obscura and *D. affinis* have been adequately
investigated.

D. melanogaster and *D. simulans* have quite clearly
not evolved very far beyond the point at which one
or the other separated off as an incipient species.
The differences between their chromosomes have
already been described (page 73). The question
arises as to whether the original cause of species-
dichotomy was the inversion in the IIIrd chromosome,
or whether this arose later, when the two forms were
already separated by the sterility-barrier in the F_1
hybrids. This question cannot be answered at
present. It is, however, extremely interesting that
the gene-differences between the two species (as
revealed by the sequence of ' bands ' in the salivary
gland chromosomes) are not distributed at random
along the chromosomes, but are concentrated in several
quite short regions. These regions are (1) the IVth
chromosome, (2) a region in the IIIrd chromosome
between the inversion and the spindle attachment,
(3) the distal end of the X-chromosome.

Now, although the frequency of mutation varies
from one gene to another, there is no reason to believe
that whole regions of the chromosomes are more
mutable than others (apart from the difference between active and inert regions). We are thus once
more driven to the same conclusion as we already

reached on entirely different grounds, namely that mutations in some regions are less lethal than in others. One may at least tentatively suggest that the regions where the differences between *melanogaster* and *simulans* lie were originally duplications which have become more and more unlike one another in the course of the differentiation of the two species.

The chromosome set of the species in the *obscura* group is entirely different from that of the *melanogaster* group (Fig. 20). It does not appear possible to homologize any large region of the chromosomes of *pseudo-obscura* with a corresponding region in *melanogaster* or *simulans*. So many rearrangements of the genetic material have taken place since the evolutionary separation of these two groups of species that no large region of any chromosome has been unaffected by inversions, duplications, translocations, &c.

The American species *pseudo-obscura* consists of two main ' incipient species ' which have been called Race A and Race B. They can be crossed but their hybrids are sterile [41] (the male hybrids completely so, the female hybrids almost completely). Physiologically Races A and B are thus almost as distinct as *melanogaster* and *simulans*; it is only the absence of definite taxonomic differences which prevents them from being regarded as separate species. They do, however, show difference in rate of development. The main cytological differences between the two races are six inversions (four in the X-chromosome and one each in Chromosomes II and III); these inversions are shown in Fig. 20. Each of the two races is subdivided into sub-races which are also distinguishable by inversions in various chromosomes, but the intraracial inversions are not identical with the inter-racial ones. The sub-races can also be distinguished by differences in the length of the Y-chromosome. In Race A four types of Y have been discovered. One of these is a chromosome with a subterminal spindle attachment (Fig. 20), another is a smaller chromosome with a median spindle attachment, the other two are chromosomes with submedian spindle attachments. Within Race B three types of Y-chromosome have been found, all with submedian spindle attachments (one of these may or may not be the same as one of the types found in Race A).

It is not possible to state exactly how these different types of Y-chromosome have arisen, but it is clear that rearrangement of sections of the chromosome has taken place, probably involving both duplication of short lengths and actual loss (' deletion ') of certain portions. Since in all races and sub-races the Y appears to be genetically inert the loss of portions of it would not affect the genic balance.

Drosophila pseudo-obscura thus appears to be breaking up into a number of ' incipient species '. Two of these are already effectively separated by the barrier of hybrid sterility, and each of these is in its turn splitting up into a number of sub-races, which, while not yet inter-sterile, will probably eventually become so. Ordinary gene-mutation appears to have played little part in the separation of all these forms which lends support to the view that it is more important as a factor in species-differentiation than in species-dichotomy.

When we come to *D. miranda* we find a species closely related to *pseudo-obscura*, but separated from it by some remarkable cytological differences.[43] The mode of sex-determination in *miranda* is unique among the species of *Drosophila* in that it involves two pairs of chromosomes, the males being $X_1 X_2 Y$, the females $X_1 X_2 X_1 X_2$. The X_1 of *miranda* clearly corresponds to the X of *pseudo-obscura*, the sequence of bands in both its arms being similar. The X_2 chromosomes, of which there are two in the female *miranda*, but only one in the male, corresponds to the IIIrd autosome in *pseudo-obscura*, and appears to have become involved as part of an entirely novel mechanism of sex-determination. There is apparently a non-random distribution of the sex-chromosomes at the first meiotic division in the male so that only two kinds of gametes ($X_1 X_2$ and Y) are formed.[41] Although all the chromosomes of *miranda* can be homologized in a general way with those of *pseudo-obscura*, a large number (100 at least) of rearrangements in the sequence of the genes have taken place. The majority of these are inversions, but some translocations of small regions from one chromosome to another have also been established. It is natural that translocations should be rarer in evolution than inversions, since they lead to the production of hypo- and hyper-diploid individuals, whilst inversions do not upset the ' genic balance '. There are indications that the arrangement of the bands in the salivary gland chromosomes of *miranda* is more similar to that in the A race of *pseudo-obscura* than to that in the B race. As in the case of the *melanogaster-simulans* pair of species the differences between the arrangement of the bands in the microchromosomes are very great.

The group of species related to *Drosophila affinis* includes at least seven species ; they are fairly closely related to the *pseudo-obscura* forms, but will not interbreed with them ; the chromosomal differences have not been fully worked out as yet.

The species *D. montium* contains two definite races (A and B) and there are probably more. The two known races differ in regard to the IVth pair of autosomes which are V-shaped in Race A and rod-shaped in Race B ; it seems clear that one arm of the IVth chromosome has been completely lost in Race B ; possibly it is genetically inert in Race A.[87] The two races of *montium* can clearly be regarded as ' incipient species '.

To sum up : we can say that the process of species-dichotomy appears to be going on at a considerable rate in *Drosophila*, so that each species is breaking up into a number of ' incipient species ' distinguished by differences in the sequence of the genes in the chromosomes, and separated by more or less complete sterility-barriers.

Conclusions

In the light of modern cytology and genetics Darwin's statement that ' varieties are incipient species ' must be modified to read ' *some* varieties are incipient species '. We have seen that in all the types of reproductory mechanism the primary origin of new species lies in some accident in the chromosome set. The occurrence of such an accident is entirely unconnected with natural selection, but if it

TABLE VIII

FREQUENCY OF DIFFERENT HAPLOID NUMBERS IN METAZOA [49]

Haploid No.	No. of Species	Haploid No.	No. of Species	Haploid No.	No. of Species
1	1	18	40	37	1
2	10	19	24	38	3
3	22	20	12	40	1
4	38	21	16	42	3
5	31	22	8	49	1
6	105	23	13	52	1
7	68	24	21	56	2
8	63	25	8	58	1
9	44	26	5	60	2
10	57	27	6	62	1
11	58	28	22	84	1
12	128	29	13	87	1
13	41	30	26	98	1
14	35	31	44	100	1
15	19	32	6	104	2
16	46	33	1		
17	14	34	3		

Total of even numbers :   644
Total of odd numbers :   426

Altogether :   1,070

is to give rise to an ' incipient species ' it must not be lethal or upset the genic balance of the organism too profoundly. If, however, the original balance is only slightly upset subsequent mutation and/or recombination of existing genes may re-establish a new ' secondary balance '. While the origin of ' incipient species ' is thus independent of natural selection, the latter is an important factor in the subsequent evolution of taxonomic differences between the new form and the original one (' species-differentiation '). Gene-mutation remains the only fundamental mechanism of morphological change in organisms, but it

TABLE IX

FREQUENCY OF DIFFERENT HAPLOID NUMBERS IN PHANEROGAMS [52]

Haploid No.	No. of Species	Haploid No.	No. of Species	Haploid No.	No. of Species
3	5	21	64	40	5
4	42	22	25	41	1
5	27	23	8	42	6
6	134	24	80	45	8
7	236	25	3	46	1
8	332	26	20	48	4
9	170	27	31	50	3
10	126	28	24	51	1
11	70	29	4	52	1
12	391	30	11	55	1
13	30	31	3	56	2
14	125	32	25	57	1
15	27	33	3	60	2
16	153	34	3	65	1
17	48	35	3	72	1
18	58	36	19	100	2
19	22	38	5		
20	47	39	1		

Total of even numbers : 1,646
Total of odd numbers : 768

Altogether : 2,414

only rarely acts as the primary origin of a new incipient species.

Most so-called diploid organisms (such as the vast majority of animal species) are really only partially diploid and that part of their gene-complex which is tetraploid is possibly less subject to the conservative effect of natural selection and is consequently in more active evolution than the rest of the genes. In bisexual animals, where polyploidy of whole chromosome sets is excluded by the sex-determining mechanism the reduplication of small segments of

TABLE X [42, 54, 86, 87, 122, 123]

DIPLOID CHROMOSOME SETS IN THE GENUS DROSOPHILA ($\male\male$)

(V = a chromosome with median or submedian spindle attachment, I = one with a quasiterminal attachment, m = a microchromosome, A = the number of spindle attachments on the assumption that V's have only one, B on the assumption that they have two.)

Species	X	Y	Autosomes	A	B
D. affinis	V	I	3 prs. I, 1 pr. m	10	11
D. ananassae	V	V	3 prs. V	8	16
D. funebris	I	I	4 prs. I, 1 pr. m	12	12
D. hydei	V	I	4 prs. I, 1 pr. m	12	13
D. melanogaster	I	V	2 prs. V, 1 pr. m	8	13
D. miranda	V, I	V	2 prs. I, 1 pr. m	8	10
D. montium (Race A)	I	V	3 prs. V	8	15
D. montium (Race B)	I	V	2 prs. V, 1 pr. I	8	13
D. pseudo-obscura (Race A)	V	V	3 prs. V, 1 pr. m	10	12
D. pseudo-obscura (Race B)	V	V	3 prs. I, 1 pr. m	10	12
D. repleta	V	I	4 prs. I, 1 pr. m	12	13
D. robusta	V	V	1 pr. V, 1 pr. I, 1 pr. m	8	12
D. simulans	I	V	2 prs. V, 1 pr. m	8	13
D. sulcata	V	V	2 prs. V, 1 pr. m	8	14
D. virilis	I	I	4 prs. I, 1 pr. m	12	12
D. willistoni	V	V	1 pr. V, 1 pr. I	6	10

chromosomes is thus of great significance, both in the origin of incipient species and in providing new ' raw material ' for evolution.

The loss of portions of chromosomes from the set must be assumed to have occurred in evolution to compensate for the acquisition of new ' duplicated ' segments ; otherwise the size of the chromosomes would have increased indefinitely in the course of evolution. Such loss probably takes place in two stages ; the regions in question first become progressively inert as a result of successive mutation and then get lost as a result of a ' deletion ' (deletions of active regions, however small, seem to be nearly always lethal in *Drosophila* when homozygous). We know next to nothing of the physical basis of inertness, but the mutation of an active gene to an inert condition seems to differ from an ordinary mutation in being irreversible. In bisexual animals duplication is the only way whereby the total number of genes can be increased, deletion the only way it can be reduced.

GLOSSARY

Allo-polyploid : An organism with more than two haploid
    sets of chromosomes which have been derived from
    two or more ancestral species, by hybridization. Cf.
    auto-polyploid.

Amitosis : A form of nuclear division in which no spindle
    mechanism is present, so that the chromosomes are
    not necessarily equally distributed to the two resulting
    nuclei.

Anaphase : The stage of mitosis which follows on metaphase
    and precedes telophase. During anaphase the chromo-
    somes move from the central region of the spindle
    towards the poles.

Aneuploid : An organism in whose somatic chromosome set
    one or more chromosomes are represented more times
    than the rest ; consequently an irregular polyploid.

Auto-polyploid : An organism with more than two haploid
    sets of chromosomes which have been derived from the
    same parent species.

Autosome : Any chromosome which is not a sex-chromosome.

Bivalent : Two homologous (or at any rate partly homologous)
    chromosomes which have paired at meiosis and are
    held together, either by a mutual attraction or by
    chiasmata.

> (*Trivalent :* a similar association of three chromo-
> somes ; *quadrivalent,* an association of four ; *multivalent,*
> an association of more than two chromosomes.)

> (*Unequal bivalent :* a bivalent in which one of the
> constituent chromosomes is longer than the other, so
> that it has an unpaired region at one end.)

Centromere : See *Spindle attachment.*

Chiasma : A visible change of pairing affecting two out of
    the four chromatids in a bivalent at meiosis ; an out-
    ward sign that a genetical cross-over has taken place.

> (*Chiasma-frequency :* the average number of chias-
> mata formed in a particular chromosome or in a par-
> ticular organism under given circumstances.)

> (*Terminal Chiasma :* an association of four chroma-
> tids end-to-end which results from the shifting of a
> chiasma until it reaches the end of the bivalent or multi-
> valent—see Fig. 14c.)

109

Chromatid : A longitudinal half of a chromosome in prophase or metaphase ; the two chromatids of each chromosome separate from each other at the anaphase of mitosis, so that a telophase chromosome consists of one chromatid only.

Chromomere : A granule on a prophase chromosome at mitosis or meiosis, or on a salivary gland chromosome. Chromomeres are now believed to be identical with genes.

Chromosome : At prophase and metaphase of mitosis, two chromatids and a spindle attachment ; at meiosis half a bivalent.

(*Branched Chromosome :* a chromosome in which the chromatids fork dichotomously, either at the spindle attachment or elsewhere.)

(*Ring Chromosome :* a chromosome in which the two ends are fused together, in such a way that a continuous circle results.)

Diakinesis : The last part of the prophase of the first meiotic division, between *diplotene* and *prometaphase.* See Fig. 9e.

Differential Segment : A segment of a chromosome which is not present in another chromosome that is otherwise homologous. The opposite to *pairing segment.*

Diploid Set of Chromosomes : A group of chromosomes which can be divided into two equal *haploid groups.*

(*Diploid organism :* an organism which has a diploid set of chromosomes in each of its somatic cells.)

Diplotene : The stage in the prophase of the first meiotic division which follows on pachytene and precedes diakinesis. See Fig. 9d.

Fixation : The process of killing and coagulating a cell by means of some chemical or physical agency.

(*Fixable :* a nucleus which can be killed and coagulated without seriously altering its visible morphology ; *unfixable :* a nucleus which is seriously altered in structure by the process of fixation.)

Heterogametic : Producing gametes of more than one kind, which differ as to the chromosomes which they contain. The opposite to *homogametic.*

Heteropycnosis : the property of contracting or condensing at a different rate from the majority of the chromosomes in the nucleus.

(*Negative heteropycnosis :* condensing more slowly than the other chromosomes do.)

(*Positive heteropycnosis :* condensing faster, earlier or more completely than the other chromosomes.)

Homogametic : Producing gametes which are all alike as to the chromosomes which they contain. The opposite to *heterogametic.*

Homologous (as applied to chromosomes) : Containing the same genes in the same sequence.

Inert Chromosome : A chromosome all or most of whose genes are physiologically inactive.

Interference : The process by which the occurrence of one cross-over or chiasma reduces the probability of another taking place in its immediate neighbourhood.

Interkinesis : The resting stage which often occurs between the end of the first meiotic division and the beginning of the second.

Interphase : See *Interkinesis.*

Inversion : A section of a chromosome which is reversed in comparison with the usual sequence.

Kinetochore : See *Spindle Attachment.*

Leptotene : The earliest part of the prophase of the first meiotic division, before pairing of the chromosomes has taken place.

Meiosis : Two modified mitoses in the course of which the chromosomes only divide once. The two divisions are called the *first* and *second meiotic* divisions.

Metaphase : The stage of mitosis which follows prophase or pro-metaphase and precedes anaphase ; when the spindle attachments of the chromosomes are lying in approximately one plane, the *equatorial plane.*

Microchromosome : A chromosome which is considerably smaller than the other members of the set, e.g. the IVth pair of chromosomes in *Drosophila melanogaster.*

Multivalent : A group of more than two chromosomes which are held together at meiosis by mutual attraction or by chiasmata.

Nuclear Sap : The substance inside the nucleus, in which the chromosomes lie.

Pachytene : The middle part of the prophase of the first meiotic division, when the pairing of the chromosomes is complete. Pachytene may be subdivided into 2-strand pachytene (before the chromosomes have split) and 4-strand pachytene (after they have split).

Pairing : The approximation of genetically homologous genes, chromomeres or chromosomes, considered either statically or dynamically. *Somatic pairing :* the more or less complete pairing of homologous chromosomes which is sometimes found at mitosis. *Zygotene pairing :* the pairing of chromosomes which takes place at the zygotene stage.

Pairing Segment (of a sex-chromosome) : A segment or short portion of a chromosome which undergoes pairing with a corresponding segment in another chromosome.

Polyploid : An organism with more than two haploid sets of chromosomes in its somatic cells.

Polysomy : A condition in which one or more chromosomes, but not the entire set are present in the polyploid state.

Pycnosis : A condition in which all the chromosomes of a nucleus have fused together to form a single mass— occurs only in moribund cells.

Quadrivalent : A multivalent composed of four chromosomes.

Ring Chromosome : A chromosome in which the two ends have fused together so that it forms a continuous circle.

Rotation (of chiasmata) : The relative rotation of the four ' arms ' of a bivalent on either side of a chiasma, which often occurs between early diplotene and diakinesis.

Salivary Gland Chromosomes : Chromosomes in the nuclei of the salivary gland cells in Diptera. These chromosomes have undergone complete somatic pairing; consequently what is ordinarily called a salivary gland chromosome is thus really two chromosomes fused side by side.

Spindle Attachment : A special region of the chromosome by which the rest of the chromosome is attached to the spindle at metaphase and anaphase. The spindle attachment is a special ' organ ' of the chromosome which can be seen at all stages of mitosis and meiosis, under favourable conditions. It does not divide at the same time as the rest of the chromosome.

Spindle Elements : The elements of which the spindle is probably composed and which usually correspond in number to the chromosomes. (*Central spindle element :* a spindle element which is not related to any of the chromosomes and which forms the ' core ' of the spindle surrounded by the other elements which lie parallel to it.

Spindle Fibres : Fibres which were supposed to exist in the substance of the spindle, running from pole to pole or from pole to equator.

Stem Body : The equatorial part of the spindle which elongates at anaphase and telophase, forming a long strand between the two resulting nuclei.

Synchronous Mitosis : The occurrence of a number of cell divisions which take place at exactly the same time in a group of neighbouring cells.

Terminalization : Shifting of chiasmata from their original positions towards the end of the bivalent.

Tetrad : See *Bivalent.*

Trivalent : A multivalent composed of three chromosomes.

Univalent : A chromosome which has not undergone pairing at the zygotene stage or one in which pairing has come to an end due to failure of chiasma-formation.

Zygotene : The stage of meiosis which follows on leptotene and precedes pachytene. The stage when pairing of the homologous chromosomes takes place.

BIBLIOGRAPHY

1 BALZER, F. 1908. Über mehrpolige Mitose bei Seeige
leiern. *Verh. d. phys. med. Ges.* Würzburg, 39.

2 BAUER, H. 1935. Der Aufbau der Chromosomen aus
den Speicheldrüsen von *Chironomus Thummi* Kiefer.
Z. Zellf., **23**, 280.

3 BEHRE, K. 1929. Physiologische und zytologische Untersuchungen über *Drosera*. *Planta*, **7**, 208.

4 BĚLAŘ, K. 1926. Der Formwechsel der Protistenkerne.
Erg. Forschr. Zool., **6**, 235.

5 —— 1927. Beiträge zur Kenntnis des Mechanismus der
indirekten Zellteilung. *Naturwiss.*, **36**, 725.

6 —— 1928. *Die Cytologischen Grundlagen der Vererbung.*
Berlin, Borntraeger.

7 —— 1929. Beiträge zur Kausalanalyse der Mitose. II.
Untersuchungen an den Spermatocyten von *Chorthippus (Stenobothrus) lineatus* Panz. *Arch. Entwickm.*,
118, 359.

8 BELLAMY, A. W. 1936. Interspecific hybrids in Platy-
poeilus : one species ZZ–WZ ; the other XY–XX.
Proc. Nat. Ac. Sci., **22**, 531.

9 BELLING, J. 1928. The ultimate chromomeres of *Lilium*
and *Aloë* with regard to the number of genes. *Univ.
Cal. Publ. Bot.*, **14**, 307.

10 BLEIER, H. 1930. Untersuchungen über das Verhalten
der verschiedenen Kernkomponenten bei der Reduk-
tionsteilung von Bastarden. *Cellule*, **40**, 83.

11 —— 1931. Zur Kausalanalyse der Kernteilung. *Genetica*, **13**, 27.

12 BONNEVIE, K. Über Chromatin Diminution bei Nema-
toden. *Jena Z. Naturwiss.*, **36**, 275.

13 BOVERI, TH. 1909. Die Blastomerenkerne von *Ascaris
megalocephala* und die Theorie der Chromosomenindi-
vidualität. *Arch. Zellf.*, **3**, 181.

14 BRIDGES, C. B. 1935. Salivary Chromosome maps.
J. Hered., **26**, 60.

15 BULLER, A. H. R. 1931. *Researches on Fungi. IV.
Observations on the Coprini, together with some investigations on social organization and sex in the Hymenomy-
cetes.* London.

[16] BYTINSKY-SALZ, H. 1934. Verwandschaftsverhältnisse zwischen den Arten der Gattungen *Celerio* und *Pergesa* nach Untersuchungen über die Zytologie und Fertilität ihrer Bastarde. *Biol. Zentr.*, **54**, 300.

[17] CANNON, H. G. 1923. On the nature of the centrosomal force. *J. Genet.*, **13**, 47.

[18] CARLSON, J. G. 1936. The intergeneric homology of an atypical euchromosome in several closely related *Acridinae* (order Orthoptera). *J. Morph.*, **59**, 123.

[19] CARNOY, J. B. 1884. *La Biologie Cellulaire* (Fasc. 1). Lierre.

[20] CATCHESIDE, D. G. 1931. Critical evidence of para-synapsis in *Oenothera*. *Proc. Roy. Soc. B.*, **109**, 165.

[21] —— 1932. The chromosomes of a new haploid *Oenothera*. *Cytologia*, **4**, 68.

[22] CHAMBERS, R. 1924. *General Cytology* (edited by Cowdry). Chicago.

[23] —— 1925. Études de microdissection. IV. Les structures mitochondriales et nucléaires dans les cellules germinales males de la Sauterelle. *Cellule*, **35**, 105.

[24] CHAMBERS, R., and RENYI, G. S. 1925. The structure of the cells in tissues as revealed by microdissection. I. The physical relationships of the cells in epithelia. *Am. J. Anat.*, **35**, 385.

[25] CREW, F. A. E. 1933. A case of non-disjunction in the Fowl. *Proc. Roy. Soc. Edinburgh*, **53**, 89.

[26] DARLINGTON, C. D. 1929. Meiosis in Polyploids. II. *J. Genet.*, **21**, 17.

[27] —— 1929. Chromosomal behaviour and structural hybridity in the *Tradescantiae*. *J. Genet.*, **21**, 207.

[28] —— 1930. A cytological demonstration of genetic Crossing-Over. *Proc. Roy. Soc. B.*, **107**, 50.

[29] —— 1931. The cytological theory of inheritance in *Oenothera*. *J. Genet.*, **24**, 405.

[30] —— 1932. The origin and behaviour of Chiasmata. V. *Chorthippus elegans*. *Biol. Bull.*, **63**, 357.

[31] —— 1932. *Recent Advances in Cytology*. (First Edition.) London and Philadelphia.

[32] —— 1934. Anomolous chromosome pairing in the male *Drosophila pseudo-obscura*. *Genetics*, **19**, 95.

[33] —— 1935. The time, place and action of crossing-over. *J. Genet.*, **31**, 185.

[34] —— 1935. The Internal Mechanics of the Chromosomes. I, II, and III. *Proc. Roy. Soc. B.*, **118**, 33.

[35] —— 1936. The limitation of Crossing-over in *Oenothera*. *J. Genet.*, **32**, 343.

[36] DARLINGTON, C. D. 1936. *Recent Advances in Cytology.* (Second Edition.) London.

[37] —— 1936. Crossing-Over and its Mechanical relationships in *Chorthippus* and *Stauroderus. J. Genet.,* **33**, 465.

[38] —— 1936. The Internal Mechanics of the Chromosomes. V. Relational coiling of the chromatids at mitosis. *Cytologia,* **7**, 248.

[39] DARLINGTON, C. D., and DARK, S. O. S. The origin and behaviour of chiasmata. II. *Stenobothrus parallelus. Cytologia,* **3**, 169.

[40] DEARING, W. H. 1934. The material continuity and individuality of the somatic chromosomes of *Amblystoma tigrinum* with special reference to the nucleolus as a chromosomal component. *J. Morph.,* **56**, 157.

[41] DOBZHANSKY, TH. 1934. Studies on hybrid sterility. I. Spermatogenesis in pure and hybrid *Drosophila pseudo-obscura. Z. Zellf.,* **21**, 169.

[42] —— 1935. *Drosophila miranda,* a new species. *Genetics,* **20**, 377.

[43] DOBZHANSKY, TH., and TAN, C. C. 1936. Studies on hybrid sterility. III. A comparison of the gene arrangement in two species, *Drosophila pseudo-obscura* and *Drosophila miranda. Z. ind. Abst. u. Vererbl.,* **72**, 88.

[44] DOUTRELIGNE, J. 1933. Chromosomes et nucléoles dans les noyaux du type euchromocentrique. *Cellule,* **42, 31.**

[45] DOZORCHEVA, R. L. 1936. The morphology of chromosomes in the Ichneumon, *Pteromalus puparum. C. R. Acad. Sci.,* U.R.S.S., 1936 (3).

[46] DUBININ, N. P., and others. 1936. Occurrence and distribution of chromosome aberrations in nature. *Nature,* **137**, 1035.

[47] DU BOIS, A. M. 1933. Chromosome behaviour during cleavage in the eggs of *Sciara coprophila* (Diptera) in relation to the problem of sex-determination. *Z. Zellf.,* **19**, 595.

[48] DUSTIN, A. P. 1921. Déclenchement expérimental d'une onde cinétique par injection intraperitonéale de serum. *C.R. Soc. Biol.,* **85**, 23.

[49] EMMENS, C. W. Unpublished work.

[50] ERNST, A. 1918. *Bastardierung als Ursache der Apogamie im Pflanzenreich. Eine Hypothese zur experimentelle Vererbungs- und Abstammungslehre.* Jena.

[51] FASTEN, N. 1914. Spermatogenesis of the American Crayfish, *Cambarus virilis* and *Cambarus immunis* (?) with special reference to synapsis and the chromatoid bodies. *J. Morph.,* **25**, 587.

[52] FERNANDES, A. 1931. Estudos nos cromosomas das *Liliaceas* e *Amarilidaceas*. *Bol. Soc. Broteriana* (Coimbra) **7**, 1.

[53] FRIESEN, H. 1934. Künstliche Auslösung von Crossing-Over bei *Drosophila*-Mannchen. *Biol. Zentr.*, **54**, 65.

[54] FROLOVA, S. L. 1936. Struktur der Kerne in den Speicheldrüsen von *Drosophila sulcata* Stert. *Bull. Biol. et de Med. Exp.*, **2**, 93.

[55] GOWEN, J. W. 1933. Meiosis as a genetic character in *Drosophila melanogaster*. *J. exp. Zoo.*, **65**, 83.

[56] GOWEN, J. W., and GAY, E. H. 1933. Gene number, kind and size in *Drosophila*. *Genetics*, **18**, 1.

[57] GRAY, J. 1927. The mechanism of cell division. IV. The effect of gravity on the eggs of *Echinus*. *Brit. J. Exp. Biol.*, **5**, 102.

[58] GREGOR, J. W., and SANSOME, F. W. 1930. Experiments on the genetics of wild populations. II. *Phleum pratense* L. and the hybrid between *P. pratense* L. and *P. alpinum* L. *J. Genet.*, **22**, 373.

[59] GROSS, F. 1935. Die Reifungs- und Furchungsteilungen von *Artemia salina* im Zusammenhang mit dem Problem der Kernteilungsmechanismus. *Z. Zellf.*, **23**, 522.

[60] GROSS, R. 1917. Beobachtungen und Versuche an lebenden Zellkernen. *Arch. Zellf.*, **14**, 279.

[61] HALDANE, J. B. S. 1931. The cytological basis of genetical interference. *Cytologia*, **3**, 34.

[62] HARRISON, J. W. H., and DONCASTER, L. 1914. On hybrids between moths of the Geometrid Sub-Family *Bistoninae* with an account of the chromosomes in gametogenesis in *Lycia* (*Biston*) *hirtaria* and *Ithysia* (*Nyssa*) *zonaria* and their hybrids. *J. Genet.*, **3**, 229.

[63] HARTMANN, M. 1929. Verteilung, Bestimmung und Vererbung des Geschlechtes bei den Protisten und Thallophyten. *Handb. der Vererbungswiss.*, **2**.

[64] HEARNE, E. M., and HUSKINS, C. L. 1935. Chromosome pairing in *Melanoplus femur-rubrum*. *Cytologia*, **6**, 123.

[65] HEITZ, E., and BAUER, H. 1933. Beweise für die Chromosomennatur der Kernschleifen in Knäulkernen von Bibio hortulanus. *Z. Zellf.*, **17**, 67.

[66] HOAR, C. S. 1927. Chromosome studies in *Aesculus*. *Bot. Gaz.*, **84**, 156.

[67] —— 1931. Meiosis in *Hypericum punctatum* Lam. *Bot. Gaz.*, **92**, 396.

[68] HUGHES-SCHRADER, S. 1927. Origin and differentiation of the male and female germ cells in the hermaphrodite of *Icerya purchasi* (Coccidae). *Z. Zellf.*, **6**, 509.

[69] —— 1930. The cytology of several species of iceryine Coccids with special reference to parthenogenesis and haploidy. *J. Morph.*, **50**, 475.

70 HUGHES-SCHRADER, S. 1931. A study of the chromosome cycle and the meiotic division figure in *Llaveia bouvari*, a primitive coccid. *Z. Zellf.*, **13**, 742.

71 —— 1935. The chromosome cycle of *Phenacoccus* (Coccidae). *Biol. Bull.*, **69**, 462.

72 HUSKINS, C. L. 1931. The origin of *Spartina Townsendii*. *Genetica*, **12**, 531.

73 HUSKINS, C. L., and SMITH, S. G. 1935. Meiotic chromosome structure in *Trillium erectum* L. *Ann. Bot.*, **49**, 119.

74 IRIKI, SH. 1932. Studies on amphibian chromosomes. VII. On the chromosomes of *Megalobatrachus japonicus*. *Sci. Rep. Tokyo Bunrika Daigaku.*, B.**1**, 91.

75 ISAWAKI, Y. 1925. Sur le déclenchement expérimental des ondes de cinèse dans le sang de quelques insectes. *Ann. de Physiol. et de Physiochem. Biol.*, **1**, 580.

76 JANSSENS, F. A. 1924. La chiasmatypie dans les insectes. *Cellule*, **34**, 135.

77 JARETSKY, R. 1928. Histologische und karyologische Studien an Polygonaceen. *Jahrb. wiss. Bot.*, **69**, 357.

78 JENSEN, H. W. 1936. Meiosis in *Rumex*. I. Polyploidy and the origin of new species. *Cytologia*, **7**, 1.

79 JØRGENSEN, C. A. 1928. The experimental formation of heteroploid plants in the genus *Solanum*. *J. Genet.*, **19**, 133.

80 JUNKER, H. 1923. Cytologische Untersuchungen an den Geschlechtsorganen der halbzwitterigen Steinfliege, *Perla marginata* (Panzer). *Arch. Zellf.*, **17**.

81 KARPETCHENKO, G. D. 1927. The production of polyploid gametes in hybrids. *Hereditas*, **9**, 349.

82 —— 1927. Polyploid hybrids of *Raphanus sativus* L. *Brassica oleracea*. L. *Bull. Appl. Bot.*, **17**, 305.

83 KIHARA, H. 1931. Genomanalyse bei *Triticum* und *Aegilops*. II. *Aegilotriticum* und *Aegilops cylindrica*. *Cytologia*, **2**, 106.

84 KIHARA, H., and ONO, T. 1926. Chromosomenzahlen und systematische Gruppierung der *Rumex*-Arten. *Z. Zellf.*, **4**, 475.

85 KIKKAWA, H. 1935. An inference as to the constitution of X-chromosome in *Drosophila*. *Proc. Imp. Acad.*, **11**, 62.

86 —— 1936. Chromosomes of *Drosophila ananassae*. *Jap. J. Gen.*, **12**, 65.

87 —— 1936. Two races of *Drosophila montium*. *Jap. J. Gen.*, **12**, 137.

88 KING, R. L. 1932. Chromosomes of three species of *Mantidae*. *J. Morph.*, **52**, 525.

89 KLINGSTEDT, H. 1931. Digametie beim Weibchen der Trichoptere *Limnophilus decipiens*. *Kol. Acta Zool. Fennica*, **10**.

[90] KOEPERICH, J. 1930. Étude comparative du noyau, des chromosomes et de leur relations avec le cytoplasme. *Cellule*, **39**, 307.

[91] KOLLER, P. C. 1932. Further studies in *Tradescantia virginiana* var. *humilis* and *Rhoeo discolor*. *J. Genet.*, **26**, 81.

[92] —— 1935. The internal mechanics of the chromosomes. IV. Pairing and coiling in salivary gland nuclei of *Drosophila*. *Proc. Roy. Soc.*, B, **118**, 371.

[93] —— 1936. The genetical and mechanical properties of sex-chromosomes. II. Marsupials. *J. Genet.*, **32**, 451.

[94] KOLLER, P. C., and DARLINGTON, C. D. 1934. The genetical and mechanical properties of the sex-chromosomes. I. *Rattus norvegicus* ♂. *J. Genet.*, **29**, 159.

[95] KOLTZOFF, N. K. 1934. The structure of the chromosomes in the Salivary glands of *Drosophila*. *Science*, **80**, 312.

[96] KUWADA, Y., and NAKAMURA, K. 1934. Behaviour of chromonemata in mitosis. II. Artificial unravelling of coiled chromonemata. *Cytologia*, **5**, 244.

[97] KUWADA, Y., and NAKAMURA, T. 1935. Behaviour of chromonemata in Mitosis. III. Metaphasic and anaphasic longitudinal split of chromosomes in the homotype division in pollen mother cells in *Tradescantia*. *Cytologia*, **6**, 314.

[98] LA-COUR, L. 1935. Technic for studying chromosome structure. *Stain Technology*, **10**, 57.

[99] LEVAN, A. 1932. Cytological studies in *Allium*. II. Chromosome morphological contributions. *Hereditas*, **16**, 257.

[100] LEWIS, W. H., and LEWIS, M. R. 1924. Behaviour of cells in tissue cultures. *General Cytology*. Chicago.

[101] LILIENFELD, F. A. 1936. Karyologische und genetische Studien an *Fragaria*. II. 1st *Fragaria elatior* eine autopolyploide Pflanze ? *Jap. J. Bot.*, **8**, 119.

[102] LUDFORD, R. J. 1936. The action of toxic substances upon the division of normal and malignant cells in vitro and in vivo. *Arch. exp. Zellf.*, **18**, 411.

[103] McCLINTOCK, B. 1932. A correlation of ring-shaped chromosomes with variegation in *Zea mays*. *Proc. Nat. Ac. Sci.*, **18**, 677.

[104] —— 1933. The association of non-homologous parts of chromosomes in the mid-prophase of meiosis in *Zea mays*. *Z. Zellf.*, **19**, 191.

[105] —— 1934. The relation of a particular chromosomal element to the development of the nucleoli in *Zea mays*. *Z. Zellf.*, **21**, 294.

[106] MAEDA, T. 1930. On the configurations of gemini in the pollen mother cells of *Vicia faba* L. *Mem. Coll. Sci. Kyoto* ·B, **5**, 125.

[107] MAKINO, S. 1932. An unequal pair of idiochromosomes in the Tree Cricket, *Oecanthus longicauda* Mats. *J. Fac. Sci., Hokkaido Imp. Univ.*, Ser. VI, **2**, 1.

[108] —— 1932. Notes on the chromosomes of *Rana temporaria* L. and *Bufo sachalinensis. Nikolski. Proc. Imp. Acad.*, **8**, 23.

[109] —— 1934. The chromosomes in *Hynobius leechii* and H. nebulosus. *Trans. Sapporo Nat. Hist. Soc.*, **13**, 351.

[110] —— 1935. The chromosomes of Cryptobranchus allegheniensis. *J. Morph.*, **58**, 573.

[111] —— 1936. The spiral structure of chromosomes in the meiotic division of *Podisma* (Orthoptera). *J. Fac. Sci., Hokkaido Imp. Univ.*, Ser. VI, **5**, 29.

[112] MANTON, I. 1935. Some new evidence on the physical nature of plant nuclei from intra-specific polyploids. *Proc. Roy. Soc.*, B, **118**, 522.

[113] —— 1935. The cytological history of Watercress (*Nasturtium officinale* R.Br.). *Z. ind. Abst. Vererbl.*, **69**, 132.

[114] MARSHALL, W. S. 1907. Amitosis in the malpighian tubules of the Walking Stick. *Biol. Bull.*, **14**, 89.

[115] MATHER, K. 1933. Interlocking as a demonstration of the occurrence of genetical crossing-over during chiasma-formation. *Am. Nat.*, **67**, 476.

[116] —— 1935. Meiosis in Lilium. *Cytologia*, **6**, 354.

[117] MATHER, K., and STONE, L. H. A. 1933. The effect of X-radiation upon somatic chromosomes. *J. Genet.*, **28**, 1.

[118] MATSUURA, H. 1935. Chromosome studies on *Trillium kamtschaticum*. II. The direction of coiling of the chromonema within the first meiotic chromosomes in the P.M.C. *J. Fac. Sci., Hokkaido Imp. Univ.*, Ser. V, **3**, 233.

[119] METCALF, M. M. 1923. The Opalinid Ciliate Infusorians. *U.S. Nat. Mus. Bull.*, No. 120.

[120] —— 1935. The germ-cell cycle in *Phytophaga destructor* Say. *Q. J. Micr. Sc.*, **77**, 285.

[121] MEURMAN, O. 1933. Chromosome morphology, somatic doubling and secondary association in *Acer platanoides* L. *Hereditas*, **18**, 145.

[122] METZ, C. W. 1914. Chromosome studies in the Diptera. I. A preliminary survey of five different types of chromosome groups in the genus *Drosophila*. *J. Exp. Zool.*, **17**, 45.

[123] METZ, C. W. 1916. Chromosome studies in the Diptera. II. Additional types of chromosome groups in the *Drosophilidae. Am. Nat.*, **50**, 587.

[124] —— 1933. Monocentric mitosis with segregation of chromosomes in *Sciara* and its bearing on the mechanism of mitosis. *Biol. Bull.*, **54**, 333.

[125] METZ, C. W., MOSES, M., and HOPPE, E. 1926. Chromosome behavior and genetic behavior in *Sciara*. I. Chromosome behavior in the spermatocyte divisions. *Z. ind. Abst. Vererbl.*, **42**, 237.

[126] MOFFETT, A. A. 1932. Studies on the formation of multinuclear giant pollen-grains in *Kniphofia*. *J. Genet.*, **25**, 315.

[127] MORGAN, L. V. 1933. A closed X-chromosome in *Drosophila melanogaster*. *Genetics*, **18**, 250.

[128] MORGAN, T. H., BRIDGES, C. B. and STURTEVANT, A. H. 1925. The genetics of *Drosophila*. *Bibl. Gen.*, **2**, 1.

[129] MORGULIS, S. 1911. Studies of inanition in its bearing on the problem of growth. *Arch. Entwickm.*, **8**, 448.

[130] MULLER, H. J. 1925. Why polyploidy is rarer in animals than in plants. *Am. Nat.*, **59**, 346.

[131] MULLER, H. J. and PAINTER, T. S. 1932. The differentiation of the sex chromosomes of *Drosophila* into genetically active and inert regions. *Z. ind. Abst. Vererbl.*, **62**, 316.

[132] MULLER, H. J., PROKOFIEVA, A., and RAFFEL, D. **1935.** Minute intergenic rearrangement as the cause of apparent gene-mutation. *Nature*, **135**, 253.

[133] MÜNTZING, A. 1930. Outlines to a genetic monograph of the genus *Galeopsis*. *Hereditas*, **11**, 267.

[134] NACHTSHEIM, H. 1913. Cytologische Studien über die Geschlechtsbestimmung bei der Honigbiene (*Apis mellifica* L.). *Arch. Zellf.*, **11**, 169.

[135] NAVASHIN, M. 1930. Unbalanced somatic chromosomal variation in *Crepis*. *Univ. Cal. Publ. Agr. Sci.*, **6**, 95.

[136] —— 1932. The dislocation hypothesis of evolution of chromosome numbers. *Z. ind. Abst. Vererbl.*, **63**, 224.

[137] NEBEL, B. R., and RUTTLE, M. L. 1935. Chromosome structure in *Tradescantiae*. VIII. The direction of coiling in *Tradescantia reflexa* Raf. as related to the mode of crossing over. *Cytologia*, **6**, 457.

[138] NEWTON, W. C. F., and DARLINGTON, C. D. 1929. Meiosis in polyploids. I. *J. Genet.*, **21**, 1.

[139] NIIYAMA, H. 1935. The chromosomes of the edible Crab, *Paralithodes camtschatica* (Tilesius). *J. Fac. Sci., Hokkaido Imp. Univ.*, Ser. VI, **4**, 59.

140 OGUMA, K. 1934. Studies on the Sauropsid chromosomes. II. The cytological evidence proving female
heterogamety in the lizard (*Lacerta vivipara*). *Arch.
Biol.*, **45**, 27.

141 —— 1932. On the chromosomes of three species of
Gryllodea. *Proc. Imp. Acad.* (Tokyo), **8**, 197.

142 OHMACHI, F. A. 1935. A comparative study of chromosome complements in the *Gryllodea* in relation to
taxonomy. *Bull. Mie. Imp. Coll. Agr. and For.*, No. 5.

143 OSTERHOUT, W. J. V. 1897. *Über Entstehung der
karyokinetischen Spindel bei Equisetum.*

144 PARISER, K. 1927. Die Zytologie und Morphologie der
triploiden Intersexe des rückgekreutzten Bastards von
Saturnia pavonia und *S. pyri*. *Z. Zellf.*, **5**, 415.

145 PATAU, K. 1935. Chromosomenmorphologie bei *Drosophila melanogaster* und *Drosophila simulans* und ihre
genetische Bedeutung. *Naturwiss*, **23**, 537.

146 —— 1936. Cytologische Untersuchungen an der hap-
loidparthenogenetischen Milbe, *Pediculoides ventricosus*.
Newp. *Zool. Jahrb.* (*allg. Zool.*), **56**, 277.

147 POLITZER, G. 1932. *Pathologie der Mitose.* Berlin,
Borntraeger.

148 PROKOFIEVA, A. 1934. On the chromosome morphology
of certain *Pisces*. *Cytologia*, **5**, 498.

149 PROKOFIEVA-BELGOVSKAJA, A. A. 1935. The structure
of the chromocenter. *Cytologia*, **6**, 438.

150 REUTER, E. 1930. Beiträge zu einer einheitlichen Auf-
fassung gewisser Chromosomenfragen. *Acta Zool.
Fennica*, **9**, 1.

151 RILEY, H. P. 1936. The effect of X-rays on the chromosomes of *Tradescantia gigantea*. *Cytologia*, **7**, 131.

152 ROBYNS, W. 1929. La figure achromatique sur matérial
frais, dans les divisions somatiques des Phanerogames.
Cellule, **34**, 365.

153 ROSENBERG, O. 1927. Die semiheterotypische Teilung
unh ihre Bedeutung für die Entstehung verdoppelter
Chromosomenzahlen. *Hereditas*, **8**, 305.

154 RUCKERT, J. 1892. Zur Entwicklungsgeschichte des
Ovarialeies bei Selachiern. *Anat. Anz.*, **7**, 107.

155 SAEZ, F. A. 1931. Cromosomas multiples en *Aleuas
vitticollis*. *Rev. d. Mus. de la Plata*, **33**, 189.

156 SAKAMURA, T. 1927. Fixierung von Chromosomen mit
siedendem Wasser. *Bot. Gaz.*, **41**, 59.

157 SANDERSON, A. R. 1933. The cytology of parthenogenesis in *Tenthredinidae*. *St. Andrews Univ. Publ.*,
No. 33. The Hague, M. Nijhoff.

158 SANSOME, F. W., and PHILP, J. 1932. *Recent Advances
in Plant Genetics.* London, Churchill.

[159] SATO, D., and SINOTO, Y. 1935. Chiasma Studies in Plants. III. Chromosome Pairing and Chiasma behaviour in the male *Rumex acetosa* with special reference to the tripartite sex-chromosome. *Jap. J. Genet.*, **11**, 219.

[160] SCHRADER, F. 1923. Haploidie bei einer Spinnmilbe. *Arch. mik. Anat.*, **79**, 610.

[161] —— 1928. *Die Geschlechtschromosomen.* Berlin, Borntraeger.

[162] —— 1929. Experimental and cytological investigations of the life-cycle of *Gossyparia spuria* (Coccidae) and their bearing on the problem of haploidy in males. *Z. wiss. Zool.*, **134**, 149.

[163] —— 1935. Some notes on the behavior of long chromosomes. *Cytologia*, **6**, 422.

[164] SCOTT, A. C. 1936. Haploidy and aberrant spermatogenesis in a Coleopteran, *Micromalthus debilis* Le Conte. *J. Morph.*, **59**, 485.

[165] SEILER, J. 1920. Geschlechtschromosomenuntersuchungen an Psychiden. I. *Arch. Zellf.*, **15**, 249.

[166] —— 1925. Ergebnisse aus Kreutzungen von Schmetterlingsrassen mit verschiedener Chromosomenzahl. *Arch. Jul. Klaus Stiftung*, **1**, 63.

[167] SOKOLOW, N. N., and TROFIMOW, I. E. 1933. Individualität der Chromosomen und Geschlechtsbestimmung beim Haushuhn. *Z. ind. Abst. Vererbl.*, **65**, 327.

[168] STERN, C. 1927. Ein genetischer und cytologischer Beweis für die Vererbung im Y-Chromosom von *Drosophila melanogaster*. *Z. ind. Abst. Vererbl.*, **44**.

[169] STEVENS, N. M. 1909. Further studies on the chromosomes of the Coleoptera. *J. Exp. Zool.*, **6**, 101.

[170] TAYLOR, W. R. 1931. Chromosome studies on *Gasteria*. III. Chromosome structure during microsporogenesis and the postmeiotic mitosis. *Am. J. Bot.*, **18**, 367.

[171] THOMSEN, M. 1927. Studien über die Parthenogenese bei einigen Cocciden und Aleurodiden. *Z. Zellf.*, **5**, 1.

[172] TORVIK-GREB, M. 1935. The chromosomes of *Habrobracon*. *Biol. Bull.*, **68**, 25.

[173] VORHIES, C. T. 1908. The development of the nuclei in the spinning gland cells of *Platyphylax designatus* (Trichoptera). *Biol. Bull.*, **15**, 54.

[174] WADA, B. 1933. Mikrurgische Untersuchungen lebender Zellen in der Teilung. I. *Cytologia*, **4**, 114.

[175] —— 1934. Über die Entstehung der Vakuolen im Kern. *Cytologia*, **5**, 248.

[176] WENRICH, D. H. 1916. The spermatogensis of *Phrynotettix magnus* with special reference to synapsis and the individuality of the chromosomes. *Bull. Mus. Comp. Zool. Harvard*, **60**, 57.

[177] WHITE, M. J. D: 1932. The chromosomes of the Domestic Chicken. *J. Genet.*, **26**, 345.

[178] —— 1933. Tetraploid spermatocytes in a Locust, *Schistocerca gregaria. Cytologia*, **5**, 135.

[179] —— 1935. Eine neue Form von Tetraploidie nach Röntgenbestrahlung. *Naturwiss.*, **23**, 390.

[180] —— 1935. The effects of X-rays on mitosis in the spermatogonial divisions of *Locusta migratoria* L. *Proc. Roy. Soc.*, B, **119**, 61.

[181] —— 1936. Chiasma-localisation in *Mecostethus grossus* L. and *Metrioptera brachyptera* L. *Z. Zellf.*, **24**, 128.

[182] —— 1936. The chromosome cycle of *Ascaris megalocephala. Nature*, **137**, 783.

[183] —— Unpublished results.

[184] WHITNEY, D. D. The chromosome cycle in the Rotifer, *Asplanchna amphora. J. Morph.*, **47**, 415.

[185] WILSON, E. B. 1905. Studies on Chromosomes. I. The behavior of the idiochromosomes in Hemiptera. *J. Exp. Zool.*, **2**, 371.

[186] —— 1905. The paired microchromosomes, idiochromosomes and heterotropic chromosomes in Hemiptera. *J. Exp. Zool.*, **2**, 507.

[187] —— 1925. *The Cell in Development and Heredity.*

[188] —— 1932. Polyploidy and metaphase patterns. *J. Morph.*, **53**, 443.

[189] WINGE, Ø. 1935. On haplophase and diplophase in some *Saccharomycetes. C. R. Lab. Carlsberg*, **21**, 77.

YAMAMOTO

INDEX

125

Printed in Great Britain by Butler & Tanner Ltd., Frome and London